THE ASTRONOMICAL
TELESCOPE

THE WYKEHAM SCIENCE SERIES

General Editors :

PROFESSOR SIR NEVILL MOTT, F.R.S.
Emeritus Cavendish Professor of Physics
University of Cambridge

G. R. NOAKES
Formerly Senior Physics Master
Uppingham School

The aim of the Wykeham Science Series is to introduce the present state of the many fields of study within science to students approaching or starting their careers in University, Polytechnic, or College of Technology. Each book seeks to reinforce the link between school and higher education, and the main author, a distinguished worker or teacher in the field, is assisted by an experienced sixth form schoolmaster.

THE ASTRONOMICAL TELESCOPE

Boris V. Barlow
Chief Design Specification Engineer
Smiths Industries Ltd

WYKEHAM PUBLICATIONS (LONDON) LTD
(A MEMBER OF THE TAYLOR & FRANCIS GROUP)
LONDON AND WINCHESTER
1975

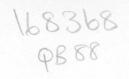
ISBN 0 85109 440 6 (Paper)
ISBN 0 85109 460 0 (Cloth)

Printed in Great Britain by Taylor & Francis Ltd.
10–14 Macklin Street, London, WC2B 5NF

Distribution :

UNITED KINGDOM, EUROPE, MIDDLE EAST AND AFRICA
Chapman & Hall Ltd. (a member of Associated Book Publishers Ltd.), North Way, Andover, Hampshire.

WESTERN HEMISPHERE
Springer-Verlag New York Inc., 175 Fifth Avenue, New York, New York 10010.

AUSTRALIA, NEW ZEALAND AND FAR EAST
(EXCLUDING JAPAN)
Australia & New Zealand Book Co. Pty Ltd., P.O. Box 459, Brookvale, N.S.W. 2100.

ALL OTHER TERRITORIES
Taylor & Francis Ltd., 10–14 Macklin Street, London, WC2B 5NF.

PREFACE

ASTRONOMY is said to be the oldest science. Development of the subject to its present level has certainly drawn upon the resources of the most modern branches of science and technology as they have arisen and the telescope has reached its present status only by the successful integration of many disciplines. The passage of time has seen an increase in the engineering content, to the extent that the large, modern telescope is primarily an engineering product designed for a critical optical purpose.

Thus it is, that after writing about some specialized aspects of telescope design, I have been invited, as a mechanical engineer with an interest in telescope development, to write this book for the Wykeham Series. If I have been at all successful it is because I have been generously assisted in fields of science and technology other than my own by advisers from observatories, centres of research and industry in many countries. The list is too long to detail, but I would especially mention the valuable help given by Mr. J. D. Pope, RGO, Herstmonceux and Dr. R. N. Wilson, ESO, TP Division, Geneva.

The presentation of the subject at this level has been greatly enhanced by the contribution and guidance of my schoolmaster collaborator, Alan Everest. I also record my thanks to my wife who typed all the unfamiliar text and correspondence without complaint.

Many of the world's most famous telescopes were made to the old, pre-metric Paris inch of nearly 27 mm, or to the Imperial inch of 25·4 mm. (Whoever heard of the 5·08 m reflector of Palomar?). I accordingly use the system of measurement (mainly to identify aperture and focal length) by which the relevant instruments are best known. The SI system otherwise prevails.

BORIS V. BARLOW

CONTENTS

ACKNOWLEDGEMENTS

THE author gratefully acknowledges assistance given by the following organizations :

Centres of Research

Department of Science, Canberra ; Dominion Astrophysical Observatory, Victoria, B.C. ; European Southern Observatory, Telescope Project Division, Geneva ; Hale Observatories, Pasadena ; Kitt Peak National Observatory, Tucson ; Lick Observatory, Santa Cruz ; Max Planck Institut für Astronomie, Heidelberg ; Mount Stromlo & Siding Spring Observatory, Woden, Australia ; National Aeronautics and Space Administration, Marshall Spaceflight Center, Alabama and Goddard Spaceflight Center, Maryland ; National Maritime Museum, London ; National Physical Laboratory, Teddington ; Observatoire de Haute Provence, Forcalquier ; Observatoire de Meudon, Meudon ; Observatoire du Pic-du-Midi, Bagnères-de-Bigorre ; Princeton University, Department of Astrophysical Sciences, Princeton, N.J. ; Recherches et Etudes d'Optique et de Sciences Connexes, Ballainvilliers ; Royal Greenwich Observatory, Herstmonceux Castle ; Science Museum, London ; Science Research Council, Radio and Space Research Station, Slough ; University of Groningen, Netherlands ; University of London, Imperial College of Science and Technology.

Industrial Establishments

Boeing Aerospace Company, Seattle ; Carl Zeiss, Oberkochen, W. Germany ; Chance-Pilkington, Pilkington Optical Division, St. Asaph ; Dilworth, Secord, Meagher & Associates, Toronto ; Ealing Beck Ltd., Watford ; Hawker Siddeley Dynamics Ltd., Stevenage ; Perkin-Elmer Corporation, Norwalk, Conn. ; Rank Precision Industries, Analytical Division, Margate ; Sir Howard Grubb Parsons & Co. Ltd., Newcastle upon Tyne.

CHAPTER 1

pre-telescope astronomy

ONE may think that to reach back thousands of years into pre-telescope history is a rather curious way to begin a short book on modern telescopes. But the earliest naked-eye observers paved the way to the subject, for modern astronomers, with all the sophisticated devices of science and technology, lean very heavily upon the recorded observations of the ancients. Indeed, one will profit by looking back almost five millennia, to an appreciation among the Chaldean and Egyptian priesthood that the night sky was ordered by some ultimate authority that commanded laws of nature, few of which were then understood. Neither were they to be understood for the next four and a half thousand years, but these priestly scholars made a valuable start some time before 2500 B.C. in the study of celestial movements. It is almost certain that their motives were more political that scientific, for the ability to measure time and forecast the rotation of the seasons gave them immense power in an agricultural community.

Precise dates for the earliest of these observations are difficult to fix, but this is unimportant. Certainly the meridian angular altitude of some prominent stars had been recorded by the Egyptians before or during the hey-day of pyramid building which flourished mainly between 2700 and 2300 B.C. All these pyramids are square-based, all have the sides of the squares oriented to the cardinal compass points and that of Cheops was so constructed that light from Sirius (the brightest star in the firmament) at each transit passed straight through a narrow shaft built into the south face of the pyramid to illuminate the mask of the deceased pharoah within for a few fleeting moments. The Pole Star at lower transit performed the same duty through a similar shaft built into the north face and also threw a lance of starlight into a further chamber deep underground through a parallel shaft. The general orientation of the Great Pyramid is shown in fig. 1.1.

The passage of 4500 years has upset the original intentions, for the combined effects of equinoctial precession and the proper motion of the stars has displaced α-Draconis, the Pole Star of Cheops's day from its reference status and substituted Polaris which today is much closer to the celestial pole and thus cannot take on α-Draconis's duty. Sirius has

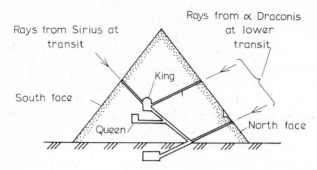

Fig. 1.1. Orientation of the Great Pyramid.

also shifted in declination during the period for the same reasons, thus leaving the royal chamber in peace and darkness now.

The ability to predict eclipse phenomena was certainly possessed by the Babylonian priesthood and there is some evidence to suggest that the Chaldeans were similarly adept about 3000 B.C. Implicit in this ability is a comprehension of the *saros*, the name given to a time interval of 18 years 10 days during which a complete cycle of eclipses occurs.

The complete geometry is very complex but fig. 1.2 shows a simplified version of the movements involved. The ecliptic plane is shown for convenience as a thin disc with the Earth which is embedded in it, in circular orbit about the Sun. The lunar orbit is represented by the series of discs inclined to the ecliptic plane and intersecting it at two points called the ascending and descending nodes, identified by a small

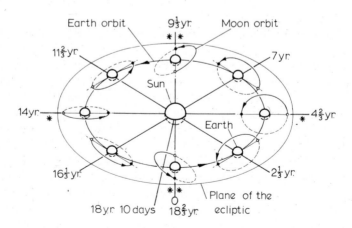

Fig. 1.2. Geometry of the saros showing the inclination of the lunar orbit to the ecliptic and the retrogressive rotation of the nodes.

2

circle and a black spot respectively. If the Moon arrives at the latter on either of the radial ordinates marked * a solar eclipse will occur, arrival at the same node at ordinates ** producing a lunar eclipse. This order of eclipse will be reversed if the Moon arrives at the alternative nodes at these ordinates and no eclipse of either kind will occur at the intermmediate ordinates. With respect to a fixed reference in space, (the reader may regard himself as this reference) the nodes complete one retrogressive revolution (that is, in opposite direction to lunar orbit) about the Earth and on the ecliptic plane in $18\frac{2}{3}$ years and thus $19\frac{2}{3}$ revolutions with respect to the Sun. Retro-rotation of the nodes and annual orbit of the Earth causes both nodes to pass through the Sun (observed from the Earth) at 342·62 day intervals. Now one mean lunation period is 29·53 days, and the lowest number of these separate events which occupy a common period is 19 and 223 respectively. The period is 6585 days, or one saros period. It follows that if, for example, the Moon is at a node which is collinear with Earth and Sun at a given time, a similar relationship will arise 18 years 10 days later and the eclipse events occurring in the period tend to repeat on a cyclic basis.

It is important to note that the diagram shows not one Earth orbit about the Sun, but one complete rotation of the nodes relative to the space reference, in eight equal increments of $2\frac{1}{3}$ years each, separated by the radial ordinates so marked. Retrogression of the nodes may be traced during this period and a saros is wholly contained within it, extending anticlockwise from ordinate ' O ' to the special ordinate marked 18 years 10 days. Thus the geometrical relationship of Earth, Moon and nodes with respect to the Sun (but not to the space reference) is the same at both ordinates.

Study of the saros tells now, as it told the early observers, that the same sequential order of eclipses will occur in any period of 18 years 10 days and because it happens that the distance between Earth and Moon (and hence the Moon's angular diameter) is very nearly the same at a given point in the saros cycle, the kind of eclipse (total, partial, annular) will also follow in the same sequence each cycle. Perturbations of a predictable nature (which need not be discussed here) do in fact vary the regularity a little.

The eclipse cycle gives us some measure of the acute powers of observation and the meticulous recording of the ancient scholars, for whichever culture unravelled the complexities of the saros, did so with equipment limited to the eyes, brain-power and a few instruments of the most primitive kind. It does not matter which process was used to expedite the unravelling, but it is doubtful whether the most erudite of the pre-Christian scholars were learned enough to be able to draw fig. 1.2 without the knowledge of why these celestial movements occur. We had to wait until the 17th century A.D. before the mysteries of planetary motion and the laws of gravitation yielded to patient pressure of enquiry. Nevertheless, at least two thousand years before Kepler and Newton and possibly two or three thousand years before that, the results of interaction between the lunar orbit and the plane of the ecliptic were known and recorded, by a contemporary élite.

At intervals throughout the development of astronomy, from the earliest Greek belief that the Sun was no more than 30 cm in diameter, (it is said, though many find it hard to believe) to the sixteenth and seventeenth centuries when astronomical discovery probably reached its peak, outstanding observers have produced inspired assessments of their personal understanding of the night sky, and of the day sky in relationship to it.

There is, for example, the hypothesis of Democritus (460–370 B.C.) who deduced the universe to be infinite and eternal five and a half centuries before Claudius Ptolemaeus (Ptolemy) took the retrograde step of enclosing it in a crystal sphere somewhere beyond the orbit of Saturn and placing the Earth at the centre. Hardened by Ptolemy's writing of the *Almagest* about A.D. 130, this format was rarely questioned during the following 15 centuries. The school of Pythagoras, contemporary with Democritus, also had the notion of a spherical universe containing a series of concentric spheres in each of which a planet was embedded, and added divine music, audible only to immortal ears, to accompany the movement of the spheres. The outer sphere bore no planet but was encrusted with the fixed stars. The philosopher Phylolaus about 400 B.C. thought that a rotating Earth could just as readily account for the apparent rotation of the heavens as the Pythagorean concept of the rotating spheres, a thought which was shared by Heraclitus who improved upon the hypothesis by putting Mercury and Venus in orbit about the Sun.

The first man to grasp the real scale of astronomical dimensions was Aristotle (384–322 B.C.), who produced a value of 400 000 stadia for the Earth's circumference, making it 19 900 km diameter compared to the modern value of about 12 600 km.

' Larger than the Moon, smaller than a star ' was his assessment of the size of the Earth.

It was Aristotle who bestowed the perfection of spheres and circles on all heavenly bodies and movements, for nothing less was good enough for the heavenly environment. And he deduced the moons sphericity from its phases, and also credited it with a surface smooth as polished marble.

4

Eratosthenes (276–194 B.C.), a native of Cyrene, improved remarkably upon Aristotle's estimate of the size of Earth by observing the meridian angular altitude of the Sun at Syene (modern Aswan) and at Alexandria, 5000 stadia (800 km) measured by professional pacers, to the north. By this process he recorded that the two cities were also separated by one fiftieth of the Earth's circumference, giving the latter a value of 40 000 km, a mere 350 km in error by modern measurement.

Aristarchus of Samos (310–230 B.C.), according to his contemporary Archimedes, anticipated Copernicus by almost 18 centuries in postulating a heliocentric universe which included a rotating Earth. He devised a method of determining the size and distance of the Moon from observation of the Earth's shadow cast upon it during lunar eclipse, and employed Greek geometry to establish similar parameters for the Sun. This involved measurement of the angle Moon—Earth—Sun at quadrature (the Moon's position at exactly half phase) at which moment he knew that the angle Earth—Moon—Sun was exactly 90°. His results lacked accuracy, giving a distance of 7·7 million km and a diameter of 64 000 km, against the modern values of 149 million km and 1·38 million km respectively.

Hipparchus, (190–125 B.C.) who knew about the retrogression of the lunar nodes but not the reason for it, was probably the greatest of the pre-Christian astronomers. He used Aristarchus's techniques to determine with considerable accuracy the lunar distance of 384 000 km and diameter of 3200 km against modern values of 381 000 km and 3460 km respectively. Similar accuracy of resolution for the Sun still proved elusive but he did improve on Aristarchus in recording a distance of a little less than 16 million kilometres.

The writings and teachings of these eminent pre-Christian scholars, the infinite universe of Democritus, and the heliocentric world of Aristarchus for example, fell before the pen of Ptolemy (about A.D. 70–160). No one up to A.D. 127–150 (the period of his studies at Alexandria) had satisfied his enquiring mind on the reasons for the wandering motion of the planets against the background of the fixed stars. This he set out to do for himself and posterity. Within the 13 chapters or books of the *Almagest*, Ptolemy laid down a most complicated geometry for the solar system as he knew it which included circular eccentric orbits, epicycles and deferents all of which provided mathematical confirmation of visual observation. Some ingenious devices were used to make the mathematics comply, bearing in mind that the Ptolemaic universe was Earth-centred and the ' planetary ' order was Moon, Venus, Mercury, Sun, Mars, Jupiter, Saturn, and beyond, the finite star sphere. Bringing Mercury and Venus inside the ' orbit ' of the Sun for example,

5

meant that they could not stray too far from it, a calculation which seemingly was confirmed by observation.

In A.D. 389 a great blow was dealt to science by the sacking and pillage of Alexandria during which the *Bibliotheca*, the great library, was destroyed. This great city had more than its share of violent strife over a period of about four centuries, starting in A.D. 274 when the Museum, equivalent to a university, was razed by order of the Emperor Aurelian, until A.D. 642 when the city fell after a year's siege to the Arabs under the direction of Caliph Omar. Earlier ravages had suppressed the development of Greek cultural thought and this final defeat ended the role of Alexandria as the seat of Hellenic culture. The Arabs, who were not short of scholastic attainment, were interpreters and translators rather than originators of new philosophy.

From this period onwards astronomical and cosmological studies shifted from the bible lands into Europe where science moved forward, more slowly it is true and sometimes clandestinely for fear of the consequences. One of the more far-sighted hypotheses of this bleak era was attributed to the Spaniard Arzachel who, at Toledo in A.D. 1070 or thereabouts, postulated elliptical orbits for the planets in order to explain their irregular movements in a far less complex manner than Ptolemy's epicylces, and thus anticipated Kepler by some five and a half centuries. So powerful was the grip of the Ptolemaic and Aristotelian hypotheses of circles, epicycles and spheres that the notion of elliptical planetary orbits was rejected by Arzachel's contemporaries.

Contact with the Greek school was re-established by the West in 1204 by the Latin conquest of Constantinople (modern Istanbul) thus making Aristotle's original work available to the West for examination, interpretation and criticism, notably at Oxford and a few years later in Paris where his teachings were forbidden until 1215.

Shortly after this period came Roger Bacon (about 1220–1292), a Franciscan friar who originally studied art in Paris but later shifted to the sciences, for he is found at Oxford in 1247 with a group of respected contemporaries studying optics, alchemy and astronomy. This is the earliest reference one finds to the study of optics unless one includes a vague reference to the work of a Muslim scientist al-Hazen in the 10th century. It is also said that Bacon came very near to inventing the telescope whilst at Oxford, although how close ' very near ' is, is difficult to assess. His reward for endeavouring to advance the progress of science brought him, like so many others, into conflict with the Church, which committed him about 1278 to the dungeons for heresy.

A century and a half after Bacon's death, Constantinople fell to the Turks in 1453 bringing about complete collapse of the Eastern Empire, and with it a welcome migration of Byzantine scholars to the West and especially to Italy.

It was in Italy that the Polish-born canon Kopernik (Nicholas Copernicus, 1473–1543) was educated, and in 1512 he discreetly circulated to a few selected friends, a small text which was destined to relax the stranglehold applied to astronomy by Ptolemy nearly fourteen centuries earlier. The paper revived the notion of Aristarchus's heliocentric universe and committed Copernicus to it. By 1539 he had worked out the structure and motion of the entire solar system as he knew it, based upon a central Sun, but with understandable timidity, withheld from publication a work of such heretical views. In the same year however he was visited by Rheticus, a professor of Wittenburg who travelled specially to speak with Copernicus and to study his manuscript and the following year Rheticus published in Danzig a review, *Narratio Prima*, of Copernicus's work where it received an encouraging if guarded reception.

Copernicus's complete work, *De Revolutionibus Orbitum Coelestium* (Revolutions of the Celestial Orbs), was finally printed under the courageous supervision of a very frightened Lutheran clergyman, Andrew Osiander, at Nürnberg in 1543. To reduce the risk of a charge of heresy, Osiander re-wrote the original preface to Copernicus's work before printing, exchanging dogma for hypothesis. Thus modified to present the reasoning as being not necessarily, or even probably accurate, but simply a mathematical device whereby calculation compatible with observation was offered, this great book was published during the year of Copernicus's death. Indeed, it is said that the proof pages did not reach the great scientist until he lay crippled with paralysis upon his death-bed. The prominent progress in *De Revolutionibus* was the establishment of a central Sun to the universe. The perfectly circular orbits of Aristotle unfortunately remained and because of this the observed variations in planetary motion made the retention of a reduced number of Ptolemaic epicycles necessary.

This important advance was all but reversed by the complete rejection of Copernicus by Tycho Brahe (1546–1601), the great but eccentric Danish observer who under the patronage of Frederick II practised his art and science with consummate skill and dedication from his observatory on the island of Hveen near Copenhagen. Copernicus's work had already shown his appreciation of the distance and nature of the stars, deduced from their lack of parallax during the annual orbit of Earth about the Copernican central Sun. Tycho on the other hand had measured the angular diameter of some of the brighter stars (with spurious results because the largest modern telescope cannot resolve the disc of the largest, nearest or brightest star) and if the Copernican distance was realistic it would have meant impossibly large stars.

Tycho's universe was Ptolemaic in derivation, based upon Earth which was central to the distant star sphere, and to the circular orbits of the Moon and the Sun. He then placed the other known planets in circular orbits about the Sun. His distinction was to be found in the accuracy of a prodigious output of recorded data which, although he did not fully understand all which he saw and measured, was to form the basis for many advanced ideas and hypotheses among those observers who followed. In order to study the movements of the seven ' celestial wanderers ' (planets) then known, Tycho located the positions of 777 fixed stars around the zodiac, a circumscribing belt of the heavens extending eight degrees above and below the ecliptic, against which to plot and meticulously record planetary motions.

It was Tycho also who discovered that the inclination of the plane of the Moon's orbit to the plane of the ecliptic is not constant and neither is the rate of retrogression of the lunar nodes, being as much as $1°$ $46'$ before or behind the mean nodal position on a cyclic basis. This discovery provides two of the several reasons why fig. 1.2 and associated text are an over-simplified presentation of the facts.

Following a quarrel with his patrons, Tycho left Denmark in 1597 to take office as Imperial Mathematician to Emperor Rudolph II in Prague. It was here that he first met and worked with Johannes Kepler (1571–1630) to whom he bequeathed his mass of observational data upon his premature death in 1601. Tycho was a great observer and recorder, but no great theorist and left the mathematical treatment of planetary motion to Kepler with the wish that he should complete this work and interpret it according to the Tychonic system. This was essentially geocentric, still enclosed in a fixed star sphere and try as he may, Kepler could not reconcile such a system with Tycho's observational data. Thus, after most imaginative treatment of the inherited material, Kepler arrived in 1609 at the First Law of planetary motion which states quite simply that the planets move in elliptical orbits about the Sun which is located at one of the ellipse's foci. Following hard upon this discovery came his second disclosure in the same year, producing the Second Law which states that the line joining Sun and orbiting planet sweeps equal areas of the orbital ellipse in equal increments of time (fig. 1.3).

The observations of Tycho Brahe were fully confirmed by these two laws and also by Kepler's Third Law which came in 1618 and which stated that the square of the orbital period of a planet is proportional to the cube of its mean orbital radius. The First and Second Laws were the result of almost eight years of mental grappling with the problem of reconciling his mathematical reasoning with Tycho's recorded data on

8

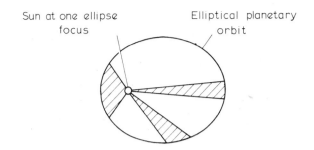

Sun at one ellipse focus

Elliptical planetary orbit

Fig. 1.3. Geometry of Kepler's First and Second Laws of planetary motion. The hatched regions are of equal area and are swept by the radius vector of the orbit in equal times.

the motion of Mars, the accuracy of which Kepler never once doubted. Success achieved, he had confidence to extend these laws to the Moon, Earth and other planets and to similarly extend the Third Law when that was formulated, all of which were confirmed by observation. In this, he had at once confirmed the centuries old hypothesis of the Spaniard, Arzachel and more importantly, had tolled the death knell for the geocentric universe of circles and spheres belonging to Aristotle and Ptolemy.

Kepler was primarily a man of the solar system and never attained a realistic appreciation of the stars as did Copernicus before him or indeed as did the Englishman Thomas Digges who in 1576 published a book in which he illustrated a heliocentric solar system and showed stars distributed to the edge of the page, elucidated by the caption, ' This orbe of starres fixed infinitely up extendeth hit self in altitude sphericallye . . . with perpetuall shininge glorious lightes innumerable, farr exellinge our sonne both in quantitye and qualitye '. One would have thought that with the writings of Democritus, Copernicus and Digges to draw upon, Kepler would have been more cognizant of the true nature of the stars, but perhaps his pre-occupation with the planets suppressed his interest in the stars except as a scale against which planetary motion could be measured.

There were others who were not so single-minded, one of whom was the itinerant Italian scholar and Copernican adherent Giordano Bruno. He heard of Digges's writings and visited England during 1583 to 1585 to learn from them and then returned to Italy in 1592 intending to teach his belief that the stars were suns with their own planetary systems. Instead, he ran headlong into the power of the church which ordered his immediate imprisonment at Campo Dei Fioro, Rome, where he languished until 1600 when he was burned alive by the Inquisition for his heretical belief in the plurality of worlds.

CHAPTER 2
development of the telescope

IN the year 1608, two young children of Hans Lippershey, a Dutch spectacle maker, had ' borrowed ' some of father's lenses to play with in their garden. Two of the lenses, one biconvex and of considerable focal length, the other biconcave and of short focal length, were accidentally arranged in optical alignment and at such separation that when one of the children peered through the biconcave lens, birds nesting in a distant church steeple were seen. It is said that Lippershey devised the world's first telescope as a result of this discovery.

In May 1609 the Italian scholar Galileo Galilei (1564–1642) heard that Lippershey had presented Prince Maurice of Nassau with a ' magic tube ', an optical device which purported to show distant objects ' distinctly as if near '. With no further information, but ' through deep study of the theory of refraction ', Galileo produced his own

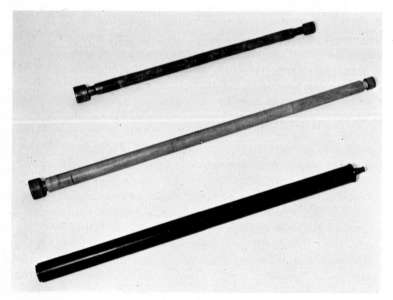

Fig. 2.1. Replicas of early telescopes by Galileo and Torricelli. *Crown Copyright. Science Museum, London.*

telescope (though the word was not coined until 1612) within days of the news reaching him. This account may be found even less plausible than that of the discovery of optical magnification by Lippershey's children, but however the ideas came to him, the Council of Venice rewarded Galileo with life professorship at Padua for his contribution to science. It is fitting that they should have done so, for whoever invented the telescope, it was certainly Galileo who first turned it to the sky. Reproductions of two of Galileo's earliest telescopes may be seen at the Science Museum, London, together with a third instrument by Galileo's contemporary, Torricelli. Figure. 2.1. is a photograph of these replicas.

1609 and 1610 were fateful years for hypotheses which had stood firm for many centuries. Galileo's first observation of the Moon for example, demolished Aristotle's notion of a polished marble sphere, for here were mountains, craters and, as he thought, seas. By the close of 1609 he had resolved the disc of Jupiter and very early in 1610 had observed four of the satellites in orbit about it, bringing to an end any idea of a Sun-centred or Earth-centred universe because to these four satellites at least, Jupiter was centre.

The Galilean telescope was then put to examination of the Milky Way which surprisingly was found to contain stars out of number, in complete accord with Thomas Digges's prophetic 'glorious lightes innumerable.' In the same year, 1610, Saturn came under telescopic examination by Galileo who explained away the oval appearance of the planet as an aberration due to the inadequacy of his instrument. Examination a short time later and at improved magnification (although evidently not improved definition) showed the planet as three contiguous stars which changed shape into a planetary disc, just like that of Jupiter, by 1612. Four years later it had grown a pair of ears like the handles on a soup bowl ! The reason for the changing form of the enigmatic planet was not to be found until forty years later, but in the intervening years there were important telescope discoveries which must not be missed.

During the closing days of 1610 Galileo realised that Venus was spherical, for his telescope showed that the planet had phases like those of the Moon, and Aristotle had declared the Moon to be spherical two thousand years earlier because of its phase display. If Venus was spherical, was it not reasonable to presume a similar form for the other planets ? Observation of Mercury was to confirm this reasoning and the improved telescopes of 30 or 40 years later showed a small phase movement on Mars, although the planet can turn very little of its darkened side towards us because its orbit diameter is greater than that of the Earth.

11

In 1611 Galileo visited Pope Paul V and Cardinal Barberini to demonstrate his telescope, an instrument technically similar to Lippershey's ' magic tube ', and to discuss the discoveries made with it. Resulting from this visit, the Pope conferred honour and everlasting goodwill upon his visitor. The goodwill did not last long however, for the year 1616 saw him summoned back to Rome to be severely censured by Barberini under direction of the Inquisition for his support of Copernicanism which he was instructed to abandon forever. This he agreed to do, but without much conviction, for in 1623 he wrote and published *Il Saggiatore* which while purporting to declare the central, stationary status of the Earth, veiled very thinly his support for the Copernican universe. Encouraged by the absence of any punitive reaction from the church, he followed in 1632 with *Dialogo dei Massimi Sistemi* in which three fictitious characters discussed the solar system and astrophysics with predictable orientation.

Papal reaction was immediate, Barberini, now Pope Urban VIII taking particular exception to being identified with one of the three characters. He was accordingly summoned to Rome once more in 1633 to stand trial before the Inquisition but escaped death by fire to be placed under house arrest at Arcetri for the remainder of his life. In 1636 he lost the sight of his right eye to be followed by total blindness a year later and on January 8th 1642, Galileo died.

Two years before Galileo's imprisonment, Kepler predicted (by application of his planetary laws) transits of both Venus and Mercury in the same year, 1631. On November 7th, using a small telescope, the French astronomer Pierre Gassendi observed the passage of Mercury across the face of the Sun, earlier by five hours than Kepler's prediction, and was amazed at the diminutive size of the planet against the background of the Sun. The transit of Venus on December 6th was obscured by cloud and was not observed. It was Kepler who, in 1611, produced the first variation to Lippershey's lens arrangement by replacing the biconcave eyepiece with a biconvex lens, located so that the focal planes of object lens and eyepiece were coincident. Such a telescope is the basis of the modern refractor but Kepler's variation suffered very seriously from chromatic aberration, which was to delay development of big refracting telescopes until the London optician John Dolland produced the achromatic doublet nearly 150 years later.

Once the initial enthusiasm had waned, contemporary scientists became dissatisfied with the telescopes they possessed and development of the instrument commenced. Towards the end of the 1630's, William Gascoigne exploited Kepler's solution, with all its faults, to improve the accuracy of angular measurement. He fixed a pair of taut crossed hairs exactly on the common focal plane of objective and eyepiece to provide a datum point in the field of view and thus a facility to align the telescope accurately with the object under observation. The invention was little known until about 1665 when it was revived and exploited by Picard. It is interesting to note that Tycho Brahe catalogued his stars to an accuracy approaching one minute of arc, that is to the very limit of naked-eye visual acuity, a value which was improved by a factor of 10 at least by Gascoigne's telescopic sight. To Gascoigne must also be credited invention of the micrometer eyepiece which consists of a movable crosswire placed in the focal plane of the eye lens. The wire is traversed across the field by a micrometer, the thimble of which is read outside the telescope. Accurate measurement of angles as small as the angular diameters of the planets was afforded by this device. The inadequacy of contemporary optical theory caused the early telescope observers a great deal of trouble which got worse as the diameter of the object lenses increased. It was however found that image quality could be improved to acceptable levels by increasing the length of the instrument in relation to the diameter of the objective (in modern terms, by increasing the focal ratio). The mechanical design of telescopes so arranged varied, but they commonly included a mast or tower and were installed out in the weather.

Of these instruments, some were made from two separate cells, one containing the object lens and one housing the eye lens. The object lens was hoisted to appropriate height on the mast, the eyepiece remaining near the ground at a height convenient to the observer's eye. Alignment and distance between the two cells was maintained by visually sighting a taut cord stretched between them. An advocate of this design was Huygens who further developed the telescope by devising the compound eyepiece (Chapter 4). With such a telescope a little less than 4 metres long he discovered Titan, the largest of Saturn's satellites, in 1655 and later in the same year, using an instrument similar in design but twice the length, solved the riddle which had confounded Galileo 40 years earlier. In 1659 Huygens published his observations and described the planet as being encircled by 'a ring, thin, plane, nowhere attached and inclined to the ecliptic.' The delay in the announcement was no doubt due to Huygens's caution in making categorical statements about an object which appeared to change its shape with the passage of time for Saturn's rings go through a cycle of visual changes lasting about 15 years.

Further detail about the rings was discovered in 1675 by Jean Dominique Cassini, director of the newly founded Paris Observatory who observed through a telescope of great length, an annular discontinuity in Huygens's 'thin, plane ring.' This dark annulus, since termed Cassini's Division was later joined by a further dusky annulus named the Crepe Ring situated on the inside edge of Saturn's ring system, discovered by W. C. and G. P. Bond in 1847 at Harvard Observatory using a 15 inch refractor.

Returning to the earlier mast-mounted equipment, an alternative to Huygens's choice was the suspension from the mast head of a rigid beam upon which were mounted the essential objective and eyepiece. The beam telescope was technically superior to the separate objective and eyepiece for it clearly facilitated more accurate and stable alignment of the optical elements. Such a telescope is shown in fig. 2.2. It is a

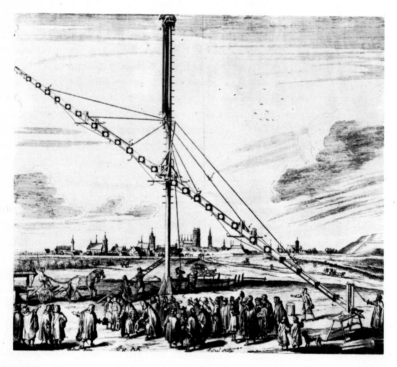

Fig. 2.2. Engraving of Hevelius's telescope at Danzig. *Science Museum, London.*

reproduction of an engraving from Hevelius's *Machina Coelestis* of 1673. Johannes Hevelius was a wealthy brewer who built and equipped a great observatory at Danzig where he practised astronomical science with distinction. The instrument illustrated was outstanding among contemporary telescopes in that it was some 40 metres long. The structure and bracing show the influence of tall ship rigging and the marine influence recurs at the base of the mast where two men are seen turning a capstan to hoist the beam by the blocks and tackle, one sheave of which is made fast to the mast-head. Fine adjustment in elevation is accomplished at the observing table by manipulation of a much smaller lifting tackle and fine azimuth adjustment is by rack and pinion which causes the eyepiece guide columns to slide laterally along the length of the bench.

By about this time, the refracting telescope had just about reached the limit of development within the confines of theoretical understanding of the subject and the quality of the optical glassware then available. It was the experimental work of Isaac Newton which eventually by-passed the problems of the refractor by producing the reflecting telescope. Newton was probably more advanced than any of his contemporaries in understanding the nature of light and particularly of the dispersion of its spectral components when transmitted through the only grade of optical glass available to him. His discoveries convinced him that perfect images in white light could never be obtained using lenses, but one principal degrading effect, chromatic aberration, could be eliminated by replacing the object lens by an object *mirror*, because as Newton knew, white light is not dispersed by reflection. These findings led Newton, at some uncertain date in the 1660's, to design and build the world's first reflecting telescope, the simplicity of which will be seen when examining ray path diagrams in Chapter 4.

The Scottish mathematician James Gregory claimed parity if not priority for the idea of a reflecting telescope, and it was unfortunate for him that the secondary concave ellipsoid mirror essential to his design was beyond the skills of the day. ·In consequence, while Gregory was postulating, Newton was building and so to Newton goes the honour of the invention.

Newton's original telescope is today in the care of the Royal Society, London, but an excellent replica is on show in the Science Museum, London, and a photograph of it appears in fig. 2.3. It is a tiny instrument, about 40 cm total height, the primary mirror being a speculum-metal (copper-tin alloy) concave paraboloid of less than 3·5 cm aperture and about 16·5 cm focal length. Note the telescopic tube with thumb-screw focus adjustment behind the mirror cell. The universal ball mounting is unique and worthy of examination. The eyepiece is seen protruding radially from the tube near the entry end. For all Newton's brilliance as a physicist (with a fair performance as a craftsman as well, judged by his telescope making) there is little evidence of his interest as an astronomical observer and one must turn elsewhere for results arising from the use of improved telescopes.

15

Fig. 2.3. Replica of Newton's original reflecting telescope. *Crown Copyright. Science Museum, London.*

But first, a reflecting telescope arrangement devised by G. Cassegrain (a French sculptor with astronomical leanings) must be mentioned. In 1672 he produced an instrument somewhat similar to Gregory's projected design of eight years earlier but susbstituted a convex hyperboloid secondary mirror for Gregory's concave ellipsoid. Both telescopes provide for observation behind the primary mirror but it is the Cassegrain system resulting in a shorter instrument which has endured, for all the largest reflecting telescopes built today include a Cassegrain system.

Three years later a remarkable discovery was made by the Dane, Olaf Römer, who was serving as assistant to Jean Picard in Paris. Römer had kept Jupiter and its four known satellites under intensive observation for a long period of time and was puzzled by an apparent variation in the orbital period of the satellites. Their eclipses and occultations slowly drifted before and then behind prediction and it was Römer who cor-

16

related the time drift with the changing distance between Jupiter and Earth as each pursued its own orbit round the Sun, Earth of course in one year and Jupiter in a little less than twelve years. The greater the distance between planets the later the satellite events took place relative to prediction and vice versa. In the year 1675, Römer made it known that the phenomenon was, in his opinion due to the finite velocity of light and further declared that light required 22 minutes to traverse a distance equivalent to Earth's orbit diameter. Today's value of a little over 16·5 minutes based on the velocity of light as 300 000 km s^{-1} indicates the extent of his inaccuracy.

Shortly after this discovery, the Royal Greenwich Observatory was founded at the command of King Charles II, who appointed John Flamsteed as the first Astronomer Royal. His primary function was to prepare astronomical data from which the navigators of the king's ships at sea could more accurately determine their positions. Flamsteed took up residence at Greenwich in 1676 and remained there until his death in 1719. During his active years at the observatory, with a 7-foot sextant and mural arc, both equipped with telescopic sight after Gascoigne, Flamsteed recorded a comprehensive series of positional observations of the Sun and Moon and catalogued the co-ordinate locations of 3000 stars to an accuracy better than 10 arc seconds. The Royal Observatory remained at Greenwich from 1676 until 1954 when atmospheric pollution and high intensity street lighting finally chased the observatory from the London area into the peaceful darkness of the Sussex countryside.

Towards the end of the 17th century a compelling need was felt for the accurate measurement of stellar distances and much of the world's astronomical skill and equipment was directed to this end. The reward was mainly frustration, for the essential parameters to be measured were mostly beyond the capability of the instruments of the day. The most elusive measurement was the annual parallax of the nearest stars, that is, a minute apparent displacement of the near stars against the background of distant stars, due to the movement of the Earth around the Sun. Nevertheless, during this abortive search, some very important discoveries were made.

For example, Edmond Halley, the second Astronomer Royal, in endeavouring to resolve the annual parallax of Sirius made the discovery that it had moved about half a degree from the location assigned to it against the distant star background by Ptolemy, 15 centuries earlier. He had discovered proper motion of the stars and went on to confirm similar motion in Arcturus and Aldebaran. Halley, who is probably best remembered for his prediction of the return in 1759 of the comet which bears his name, died in 1742 to be succeeded at Greenwich by James Bradley.

It was Bradley who in his search for evidence of annual parallax in the middle 1720's discovered the aberration of light, an apparent annual fluctuation of stellar positions due to the effect of the orbital velocity of Earth and the finite velocity of light. This can be regarded as similar (on a different scale) to the apparent slope of the path of the raindrops if one looks sideways while walking swiftly through a shower of vertically falling rain. The extent of the aberration is greatest for stars lying in a direction perpendicular to Earth's motion in orbit and is then termed the constant of aberration amounting to an apparent displacement of about 20·5 arc seconds. From this Bradley was also able to estimate the velocity of light, and gave the time required for sunlight to reach the Earth as 8 minutes 13 seconds, a decided improvement on Römer's value of 11 minutes obtained six decades earlier.

Around the middle of the 18th century, two London master opticians applied their expertise to the improvement of telescope optics. One was James Short who, from about 1735, made speculum mirrors of very high quality and, more importantly, to definite mathematical profiles. He was thus able to make, (indeed he preferred to do so), telescopes of Gregorian design which had been beyond the skill of Gregory. Short produced a great number of telescopes of this kind ranging from the tiniest ' pocket ' portable to observatory giants (of the day) up to nearly 50 cm linear aperture, and supplemented the range by building Cassegrain instruments as well.

The first serious opposition to the supremacy of the 18th century reflecting telescope came from John Dolland who in about 1755, succeeded in reducing chromatic aberration in the refracting telescope to acceptable levels. He produced the achromatic doublet object lens in which the chromatic aberration of a convex crown glass lens is substantially corrected by a concave flint glass lens behind it, so bringing white light images to acceptable sharpness at the focal plane of the doublet. In addition, the lens surfaces were so curved that a rewarding reduction of spherical aberration was also obtained. Dolland produced and sold many such telescopes, most of them fairly small and all of them very expensive.

Too small and expensive for William Herschel, that remarkable character who, in 1773, turned to astronomy from a career in music at the age of 35 years ! His early work was carried out with conventional uncorrected refractors of the day, but the work which he had in mind could not be accomplished with these instruments and under the compelling influence of necessity he came to distinguish himself as a telescope maker as well as an astronomer. His instruments were each equipped with a speculum-metal primary mirror cast and worked by his own hand. These objectives, hard, brittle and receptive to a very high polish, produced brighter images when new than did refractors of similar aperture.

His work on double stars and the inevitable search for annual parallax was carried out mainly with two such telescopes, one of 6 inch aperture and 72 inch length, the other of 19 inch aperture and 240 inch length. In the year 1781, whilst endeavouring to record annual parallax in an optical double star using the smaller of the two telescopes, he discovered the planet Uranus, seen and recorded without recognition by Flamsteed, Bradley and others at least 17 times previously. Herschel's observation however showed it as a misty but perceptible disc. In the year 1802 his search for annual parallax produced a further by-product in the discovery of binary stars, that is, two stars in relatively close proximity to each other and in orbital motion about a common mass centre, as distinct from the optical doubles which only appear to be associated but are in fact separated by immense distance in the line of sight. Such work led Herschel to wish for, and in 1789, to complete, his great telescope of 48 inch aperture and 480 inch focal length. Figure 2.4 shows a contemporary engraving of the instrument in which the engineering skills embodied will be apparent. This instrument, which did so much to open up extra-galactic space, held its position as the world's largest telescope for 56 years until 1845 when it was displaced by ' The Leviathan of Parsonstown,' a telescope of 72 inch aperture and 720 inch focal length built by William Parsons, Earl of Rosse, at Parsonstown in Ireland.

The great tube of Rosse's telescope, mounted between thick masonry walls which restricted manoeuvrability very considerably, did great work during its active life in unravelling the structure of the spiral galaxies. This telescope was the last of the big speculum reflectors for as the size increased so did the optical aberrations due to thermal distortion of metallic mirrors. This defect, coupled with steadily increasing size and improved performance of the achromatic refractors brought the latter to popularity at the expense of reflector development at the time.

In the early part of the 19th century flint glass discs of flawless quality and of diameter greater than 4 inches were rare indeed, and even by 1830 the largest achromatic refractor in America was a 5 inch instrument made by Dolland's son Peter for Yale University. The secret of making flint glass discs of optical quality was evidently discovered by the Swiss, Pierre Guinand who managed to make discs up to 10 cm diameter and more, by the closing years of the 18th century. The products of the

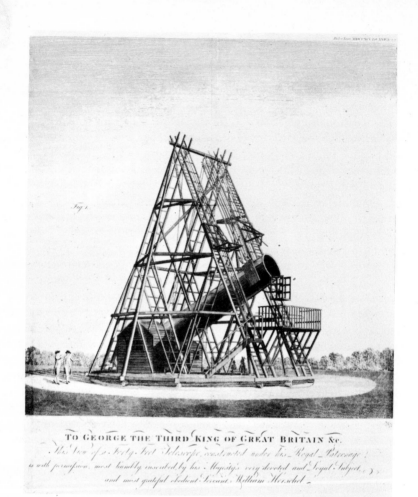

TO GEORGE THE THIRD KING OF GREAT BRITAIN &c.

*This View of a Forty Feet Telescope, constructed under his Royal Patronage,
is with permission, most humbly inscribed by his Majesty's very devoted and Loyal Subject,
and most grateful obedient Servant, William Herschel.*

Fig. 2.4. Engraving of William Herschel's 48 inch reflecting telescope at Slough. *Science Museum, London*

closely guarded secret were eventually made available by Guinand's association with Joseph von Utzschnieder who owned a Munich glassworks.

Joseph Fraunhofer was a youthful glassworker at the Munich factory and it was he who was entrusted with working the rare, large flint glass discs into finished lenses of very fine quality. It was Fraunhofer also who devised the German equatorial mounting which is almost universally applied to medium and large refractors to this day. It was a Fraunhofer refractor with which Argelander fixed the co-ordinate

20

positions and magnitudes of 324 198 northern stars over a period of a quarter century from 1837. One of the most famous equatorial refractors was the 9½ inch telescope at Dorpat (modern Tartu) in Estonia, completed by Fraunhofer in 1824. It remained the world's largest refractor until 1847.

With this instrument, the German Wilhelm Struve took up double star astronomy where Herschel left off and expanded the latter's catalogue of 800 double stars to 3110. With this instrument also, Struve at last succeeded in measuring annual parallax, announcing with excessive precision in 1839 that he had traced a real annual parallax in the bright star Vega, of 0·2605 arc seconds. Others soon followed his lead. Thus we have Friedrich Bessel using a 16 cm Fraunhofer heliometer at the Konigsberg Observatory, announcing with equal excess, that the faint star 61 Cygni, had annual parallax of 0·3483 arc seconds. Meanwhile, Thomas Henderson, then working at the Cape Observatory, turned his attention to the bright southern sky double star alpha Centauri. Upon returning home to his native Scotland, he analysed the collected data and announced a more reasonable assessment of about one arc second for its annual parallax, which established it as our nearest star (Sun excluded) at a little more than four light-years distant. Other astronomers were quick to join the search but Struve had just about reached the limit of trigonometrical distances in the measurement of Vega. For this reason, the next 60 years or so to 1900 produced a mere 80 parallax results, many of them of doubtful accuracy.

The year 1864 saw William Huggins consolidate astrophysics as a separate branch of telescope astronomy, for using the discoveries made by Fraunhofer, and by Bunsen and Kirchhoff, between about 1815 and 1860, he established that the nebulae in Draco and Orion were composed mainly of incandescent gas whilst the nebula in Andromeda was a star cloud. Huggins's private London observatory was equipped with a fine 20 cm equatorial refractor which he modified to focus the image upon a slit behind which two prisms were so placed as to disperse the transmitted light into a spectrum. The slit, prisms and a few small lenses required to cast a sharp image of the spectrum combined to form a separate instrument called a spectroscope (see Chapter 7). With this instrument, Huggins and his colleague William Miller were able to compare the spectra of the stars and nebulae with those of incandescent gases in the laboratory and the comparison revealed that the universe within reach of the telescope was reassuringly made up of elements already well known to us.

Spectroscopy was as significant a scientific advance as the discovery of the telescope had been 250 years earlier, and to it was added the immense advantage of photography in 1876, again by Huggins who took the first successful photograph of the spectrum (a spectrogram) of the bright star Vega. The advent of the photographic dry plate towards the end of the 19th century gave considerable impetus to astronomy but the available telescopes were not extracting maximum advantage from the new technique, for all the existent refractors were corrected for work ranging over the visible spectrum. The photographic plates however, were insensitive at the red end and most sensitive at the blue and thus required achromatic objectives corrected for maximum performance in this region. Reflectors did not suffer this shortcoming but all types suffered from inadequate mountings, for whilst the eye did not register the inadequacies, the prolonged exposure photograph certainly did. Lack of synchronism in the sidereal drive which was commonly hand or clockwork powered until as late as 1940, resulted in all the star images being recorded as arcuate traces concentric with the celestial pole whilst general flexibility in mounting and tube degraded the star images into planet-like discs.

Meanwhile, the provision in 1847 of a 38 cm refractor for Harvard College Observatory by the German firm, Merz and Mahler, (the instrument used by W. C. and G. P. Bond in the discovery of Saturn's crepe ring) stimulated the American, Alvan Clark to develop a distinguished business in conjunction with his sons George and Alvan, which produced the best telescopes in America, culminating in the manufacture of the objectives for the 36 inch Lick and the mighty 40 inch Yerkes refractors, the latter remaining to this day the world's largest steerable refracting telescope.

During this period, two notable refractors were installed at the Royal Greenwich Observatory. One, a 32·5 cm instrument by Merz & Son of Munich was installed in 1860 upon an equatorial mounting designed by George Biddel Airy, seventh Astronomer Royal. The Merz telescope was replaced in 1893 by a 28 inch instrument by Sir Howard Grubb of Dublin (on the original mounting) which is still rated as the world's seventh largest refractor. It was dismantled complete with its mounting in 1947 and re-erected ten years later at the Royal Greenwich Observatory site at Herstmonceux, Sussex, where the photograph of fig. 2.5 was taken. The dome it occupied is, at the time of writing, required for a modern wide angle telescope, but happily the great Grubb refractor with its Airy mounting has been returned to the original Greenwich site under the care of the National Maritime Museum for reinstatement by the end of 1973, for the use of accredited professional and amateur observers.

With the completion of the 40 inch Yerkes instrument, steerable

Fig 2.5. 28 inch Grubb refracting telescope at the Royal Greenwich Observatory, Herstmonceux Castle. *National Maritime Museum, London.*

refractors reached the limit of size, because refractor aperture is limited by weight of the glass object lens which sags in varying manner with changing attitude of the telescope. The resulting deformation of lens curvature so degrades refractive performance that telescopes beyond the size typified by the Yerkes instrument are impractical.

But in the 1850's reflector development resumed when Karl A. von

Steinheil and Leon Foucault produced a new form of mirror from an optically worked glass disc, more easily cast, lower in thermal expansion than speculum-metal and surface silvered by a simple chemical process on the worked face. Mirrors can, of course, be supported by structures behind them to maintain accuracy of profile in any attitude of the telescope within limits. Such mirrors were installed in the 60 inch reflector at Mt. Wilson in 1908 and in the giant 100 inch Hooker instrument at the same observatory in 1918, the world's largest telescope at the time. Using it to the limit of its capacity a few years later, Edwin Hubble resolved, in the peripheral regions of the spiral galaxies M31 and M33, a number of cepheid variable stars, originally discovered in our own galaxy in 1912 by Miss Henrietta Leavitt. Both telescope discoveries were of immense importance, Miss Leavitt's for providing a yardstick for astronomical distance measurement and Hubble's for using it in fixing the distance of both Messier galaxies at about 900 000 light years each, and thus clearly external to the Milky Way.

It was with the 100 inch telescope that Francis Pease in 1920 measured the diameter of the bright star Betelgeuse in Orion. He used an optical arrangement devised by Michelson (Chapter 7) which increased the effective aperture of the telescope and produced an interference fringe pattern from which the star's apparent angular diameter was deduced to be 0·051 arc seconds, giving a linear diameter of about 340 million kilometres. As it happened, Betelgeuse was an unfortunate choice for it is now known to be a pulsating star, the diameter of which varies within the ratio limits of 1–1·4.

George Ellery Hale was the distinguished American astronomer who, in the late 1880's at his private observatory at Kenwood, devised a new instrument, the spectroheliograph which, in conjunction with his 12 inch refractor enabled him to take photographs of the Sun in monochromatic light. The resultant 51 mm diameter solar image dissatisfied Hale, who then built a larger spectroheliograph for attachment to the 40 inch Yerkes refractor, yielding a 178 mm diameter image. Still dissatisfied, he established the observatory at Mount Wilson where he installed several long-focus, fixed-position solar telescopes which eventually yielded solar images up to 40 cm diameter. Two of these telescopes, one of 60 feet focal length and the other of 152 feet focal length, are in regular use today.

A great deal of solar research was executed in the first half of the present century and a lot of new equipment was designed for this purpose. Thus we have Hale's development of the spectroheliograph into the spectrohelioscope which facilitated visual observation of the solar prominences and flares and Bernard Lyot's introduction in 1930 of the

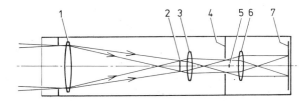

Fig. 2.6. Ray path of Lyot's coronagraph. (1) Objective, (2) Eclipse disc, (3) Field lens, (4) Diaphragm, (5) Mask, (6) Camera lens, (7) Plate.

coronagraph with which photographs of the solar corona are made without the need to wait for a total eclipse of the Sun, as was previously necessary. Figure 2.6 is a schematic diagram of Lyot's coronagraph in which the objective 1, forms an image of the Sun upon the opaque eclipse disc 2, fitting it exactly. The field lens 3 forms an image of the objective at the plane of the diaphragm 4, which is there to intercept diffracted light from the edge of the objective. The mask 5 intercepts a central spot of light caused by reflections of sunlight from the surfaces of the objective, and the camera lens 6 focuses the light of the corona upon the photographic plate 7. Figure 2.7 is a photograph of the inner corona, filtered to exclude all but hydrogen alpha (red) light, taken with such an

Fig. 2.7. Photograph of the Sun's inner corona in H_α light taken with the coronagraph in the absence of a natural eclipse. *Observatoire du Pic-du-Midi.*

instrument at the Pic-du-Midi high altitude observatory without the assistance of a natural eclipse.

In the same year, 1930, an Estonian, Bernard Schmidt, produced the Schmidt camera, an instrument in which reflecting and refracting elements are used in combination to form the primary image (see Chapter 4). Until fairly recently its function has been wholly photographic, in which it excels because it combines large linear aperture with very low focal ratio and high definition over a wide angular field. Schmidt's original instrument included a linear aperture of 35 cm, focal ratio of $f/1.7$ and a field semi-angle of $8°$ in its specification. This type of instrument has since been developed in size to culminate in the great camera at Palomar Observatory, of 48 inch linear aperture and field semi-angle of $3°$ covering a photographic plate 14 inches square.

1934 saw a considerable advance in the treatment of the reflecting surfaces of telescope mirrors when surface silvering retreated before the advance of vacuum deposition of aluminium. The process consists of enclosing the mirror in an evacuated chamber and electrically evaporating a small quantity of aluminium within the chamber. The resulting perfectly uniform thin film coating is harder and less prone to tarnish than silver and is more reflective in the shorter wavelengths. The great 200 inch Hale reflector of Palomar, unchallenged for size since it was commissioned in 1948, is equipped with a low-expansion, surface-aluminized Pyrex glass mirror. It has been worked hard and successfully over the years, mainly on extra-galactic research.

However large and however perfect the earthbound telescope, there is always atmosphere above it to degrade performance. Hale lifted heavy equipment to the top of a mountain to escape from some of it. For his solar observations, Lyot preferred the thin air of Pic-du-Midi at an altitude of 2860 metres above the sea, to more accessible locations. But in 1957 Martin Schwarzchild, of Princeton University, launched the first unmanned telescope to leave the ground, to stratospheric altitude suspended beneath an enormous balloon. Details of this and subsequent flights are given in Chapter 10, together with brief accounts of the ultimate high altitude flights, the space telescopes.

Looking back through the preceding pages one sees that when the early refractor reached the limit of performance, progress was maintained by the introduction of the reflecting telescope fitted with a speculum-metal main mirror. When thermal expansion and production difficulties limited progress along this avenue, the achromatic objective was available until it reached an order of size where its own weight halted refractor development once more. Next came the low-expansion glass mirror which has allowed construction of telescopes up to the size of the giant Russian instrument of 6 m aperture, at present in progress. It is difficult to imagine development of ground-based telescopes beyond this size, but it is possible that improved performance in telescopes of a given aperture may be attained by the development of modern glass/ceramic compounds, which have excellent thermal characteristics and crystalline structure. There is also space to be exploited and quite apart from the smaller instruments in space now, a telescope of 120 inch aperture, large even by ground-based standards, is scheduled for launch into Earth orbit in 1980.

CHAPTER 3

some basic optics

THE radiation collected by the telescope brings to the observer information about a star's chemical composition, its temperature, motion, distance and other properties and attributes. This chapter outlines briefly the nature of this radiation, how it can be collected and directed by mirrors and by lenses, and the limits that are set to the performance of these optical elements by their own properties and by the wave nature of this radiation.

3.1. *Electromagnetic waves*

A wave is characterized by its frequency ν and wavelength λ, and while it travels through a medium in which its velocity is v the relation $v = \nu\lambda$ always holds. The frequency is determined by the source and is fixed once the wave has set out ; the wavelength then depends on the velocity of the wave in the medium being traversed, and can vary along the path of the wave. What is being propagated is an *oscillating change* in some quantity, which is capable of storing energy in the medium and passing it on through the medium. The amplitude of a wave of the ordinary kind is the greatest departure of the quantity from its mean value as the wave progresses ; the rate at which the wave carries energy is proportional to the square of the amplitude.

All bodies radiate energy in the form of electromagnetic waves. These can travel through a vacuum, the energy being handed on, not by vibrating particles, but by oscillating electric and magnetic fields, the frequency of oscillation being the frequency of the waves. The velocity of all electromagnetic waves in a vacuum is the same, the value being about 3×10^8 m s^{-1} (usually represented by c). In any material medium $v < c$, so $\lambda_{\mathrm{medium}}/\lambda_{\mathrm{vacuum}} = v/c$. In air, v is only a little less than c so that for most purposes we take v_{air} to be the same as c, though the difference is sometimes very important. Radiation supposed to be of a single wavelength λ (in practice, lying within a narrow band $\Delta\lambda$ centred upon λ) is called monochromatic.

All the electromagnetic radiation from any source originates as bursts of monochromatic radiation which last for about 1 ns and so form a wave-train of length about 30 cm (the coherence length). Each of these bursts is a single entity carrying a definite quantity of energy depending on the frequency; it is called a *photon* when we think of it as a wave-train or wave-packet or particle, and a *quantum* when we think of the energy that it conveys. A photon of frequency v (in Hz) carries a quantum of energy hv (in J), where h is the Planck constant, value $6 \cdot 63 \times 10^{-34}$ J s.

For visible light, the wavelength range is from about 380 nm (violet) to 760 nm (red); in decreasing wavelength order beyond the violet come ultraviolet, X-rays and γ-rays, while in increasing wavelength order beyond the red come infrared and radio waves.

Some sources, such as excited atoms in a discharge tube (or in the outer layers of a star) concentrate most of their radiation into a few monochromatic ' lines ' which are characteristic of the source and of the way in which they have been excited. But bodies also emit a continuum of wavelengths simply because they are at temperatures above absolute zero. This radiation depends very much more on the temperature of the body than on the nature of the body itself, and in the ideal case (approximated to in practice by the walls of a specially shaped cavity formed in a block of carbon) it depends only on the temperature. It is then called ' temperature radiation ', ' full radiation ', or more usually nowadays ' black body radiation '. Most stars (for our purposes) approximate to black bodies.

At all temperatures, all possible wavelengths are represented (if in practice this does not happen, the radiator is not quite a black body). For a black body at temperature T, the total power radiated per unit area is proportional to T^4 (Stefan's law). The power distribution

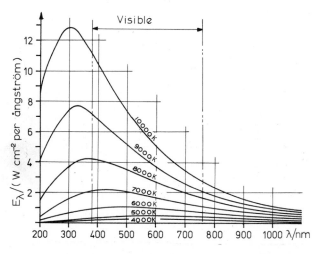

Fig. 3.1. Black-body curves for stellar temperatures.

29

(strictly, the distribution of E_λ, the power-per-unit-wavelength-interval) is as shown in fig. 3.1, the Planck distribution ; the peak of the curve λ_{max} moves steadily towards the short-wavelength side as T increases. And the relation between λ_{max} and T is given by Wien's displacement law, $\lambda_{max}T = $ a constant. The surface temperatures of most stars are such that wavelengths in the visible spectrum are strongly represented, and in the case of our own Sun (T about 5800 K) λ_{max} is about 500 nm.

3.2. Huygens' construction

As a wave travels, each point in the medium along its path undergoes the same periodic disturbance, but later in time the further the point is from the source. And as the disturbance passes each point, that point hands it on to points further along the path, just as if (from their point of view) it were itself a source. A wavefront is the locus of all those points in the medium which are in exactly the same phase of oscillation. For a point source which is radiating in all directions the wavefront is a sphere centred on that point, represented as a circle in fig. 3.2, where B represents a wavefront that has originated at A. To find out where

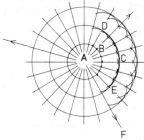

Fig. 3.2. Huygens's construction for propagation of light.

this wavefront will be at time t later, we consider every point on B to be the source of spherical wavelets spreading out in all directions, of radius vt. The only places where they are all in phase in the direction of travel are on the sphere D which envelops them. This is then the new wavefront. Propagation is thus in a direction normal to the wavefronts and is represented by the radial lines AF etc. which are called *rays*.

Every secondary wavelet from *the whole* of the spherical wavefront is needed if the new wavefront is to be spherical also, with the rays spreading out radially. If part of the wavefront is allowed to proceed through an aperture, or if part of the wavefront is obstructed by an opaque obstacle, then secondary wavelets spread round the edge of the aperture or obstacle so that the rays also spread beyond the edge, an effect called diffraction. In fig. 3.3, the shadow de of the opaque disc bc, and the light-patch hj from the circular hole fg are not as sharp at the edges as straight-line ray propagation from the source A, would lead one to expect. The effect is usually very small, and for an aperture of diameter d and light of wavelength λ it depends on the ratio $\lambda\,d$.

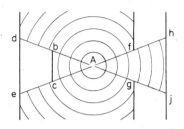

Fig. 3.3   Rectilinear propagation of light from a small source A.

Image formation

We consider only the formation of a real image on a screen (fig. 3.4). Light from a point source, or from a point on an extended illuminated object, passes through the small aperture A, when individual *pencils* bd, ce, etc. from points on the object BC form small patches of light to give an inverted image DE on the screen. The image will always be formed, wherever the screen is and whatever the distance of the object, for these distances govern only the ratio of the image size to the object size, since $h'/h = a'/a$. The smaller the aperture A, the smaller each light patch will be, and the more sharply resolved will be the detail in the image, until a limiting diameter of aperture is reached. Reduction of aperture size beyond this limit results in degraded image sharpness due to diffraction effects (see fig. 3.12, p. 39). Pinhole apertures produce dim images, but this can be improved if the pinhole is replaced by a

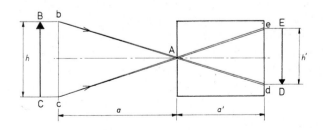

Fig. 3.4.   Principle of the pinhole camera.

31

converging lens of much greater aperture, which will focus each pencil to an approximate point upon the plate, the position of which is very strictly governed by the distance of the object.

3.3. *Regular reflection*

The incident and reflected rays and the normal to a reflecting surface at the point of incidence lie in the same plane, and the incident and reflected rays make equal angles with this normal. In wavefront terms, Huygens' construction (fig. 3.5) shows the process of reflection of

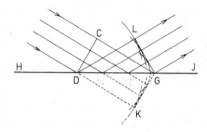

Fig 3.5.   Reflection at a plane surface.

plane wavefronts at a plane surface ; CD represents a plane wavefront at the instant when the edge D reaches the surface HJ ; GK is the position that the wavefront would have reached if the surface HJ had not been there, and LG the reflected wavefront at the instant when the edge C reaches the surface and reflection is complete. And fig. 3.6 illustrates the formation of an image by a spherical concave mirror. Light diverging from the object point A on the axis of the mirror sends spherical wavefronts towards the mirror surface BDE, which has its centre of curvature at C. The wavefront BD'E first meets the mirror at its edges B and E. If the mirror were absent, by the time the central ray AD' had reached the point D, the wavefront would have reached GDH. But during this time a wavelet of radius BG will have proceeded from B and further wavelets originating from all points on the mirror surface will have generated the reflected wavefront JDK. The radius of each such wavelet is the distance between the mirror surface and the wavefront GDH measured along the line of any ray within the angle BAE. This construction gives the *exact* shape of the reflected wavefront, and if the relative aperture is small, the wavefront can be treated as spherical and converging to an image point. If the object is distant, and only the paraxial part of the mirror is used, then the reflected wavefront can

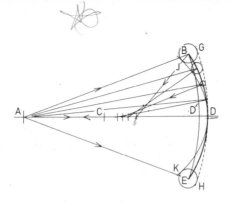

Fig. 3.6. Reflection at a curved surface.

be regarded as converging to an image point. The paraxial region of the mirror is a very small circular area of the mirror centred on its axis, and a parallel pencil of rays incident on this region from a distant object point on the axis is said to be composed of paraxial rays. The image point is at the focus, halfway between the mirror surface and the centre of curvature.

We shall not try to show the wavefront construction, but it is a property of the paraboloid (the surface formed by rotating a parabola about its axis) that all rays striking a paraboloidal mirror parallel to the axis are reflected to a single point on the axis, the focus of the surface, however wide the aperture used, that is, the rays need not here be confined to paraxial rays. So a paraboloidal mirror forms a sharp image at its focus of a bright distant object point on the axis, however big its aperture. This is the classical form of a telescope primary mirror (frequently modified in modern designs, see chapter 4) which can thus form the sharp image of a star at the prime focus when the star, and hence the image, both lie on the mirror axis.

3.4. *Refraction*

Refraction occurs at the boundary between two media in which light travels with different speeds. The absolute refractive index of a medium n, is defined by the equation $n = c/v$. The relative refractive index for the boundary between two media, with the light travelling from the 'first' (n, v) to the 'second' (n', v'), is $v/v' = n'/n$. If the first medium is air, for which n is about $1 \cdot 00029$ under ordinary conditions at sea level, the relative refractive index n'/n for glass can be taken as n for most purposes. For a ray of light striking the interface between two media at an angle i to the normal, the angle of incidence, and being refracted into the second medium at an angle i' to the normal, then $n'/n = \sin i/\sin i'$ (Snell's law).

33

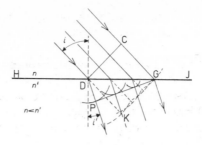

Fig. 3.7.　Refraction at a plane surface by Huygens's construction.

In fig. 3.7, Huygens's construction is used to follow the refraction of a plane wavefront at a plane boundary.　Here the edge D of wavefront CD has just reached the boundary HJ between two media.　If HJ had not been there, the wavefront would have travelled to GK with velocity v during the time it takes C to reach the boundary.　But as each part of the front reaches HJ, the secondary wavelets spread out with v' into the second medium, whence we can construct PG, the envelope of the secondary wavelets at the instant when refraction of the pencil is complete.

In fig. 3.8, a parallel pencil ABDE from a point on a distant object is incident on the spherical refracting surface FGH which has its centre of curvature at C.　The plane incident wavefront DGE first meets the refracting surface at G and is retarded so that in the time required for the edge D of the wavefront to reach the point F on the surface, the centre, G, of the wavefront will only have travelled to J and not to K which would have been reached in the absence of the refracting surface. So the initial plane wavefront leaves the refracting surface as a concave wavefront FJH, the rays of which converge to focus at the point L on the

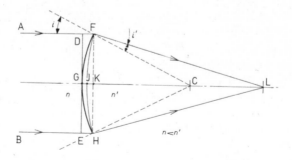

Fig. 3.8.　Refraction at a curved surface.

34

image. From the law of refraction, $n \sin i = n' \sin i'$, and if only the paraxial region of the surface is considered, i and i' are small, hence $ni = n'i'$.

These results may be used to trace the ray-paths, and hence the changing shape of the wavefront through any curved surfaces, for example, a biconvex converging lens which has both surfaces as parts of spheres centred on the optical axis of the lens. Since $v' < v$ the longer the glass-path traversed by a given part of the wavefront, the more it will trail behind those parts which traverse shorter glass-paths. So, because the thickness at the centre of the lens is greater than the thickness at its edge, an incident plane wavefront normal to the axis of the lens will, after transmission through it, emerge as a concave wavefront the rays to which converge to a point on the axis called the principal focus, F, at a distance called the focal length, f, from the lens. It is important to note that this is true only if the lens is thin, that is, if its thickness is small compared with its aperture, and if paraxial rays only are considered.

The performance of thick lenses, and lenses which converge the rays at the edge of the aperture to a common focus with those in the paraxial region, may be found by using the described construction, but the process is complicated by the usually required aspheric profile of the lens surfaces. An aspheric surface is one which is not a part of a sphere. Ray-paths may also be traced through compound lenses consisting of two or more single lenses (singlets) assembled on a common optical axis for specific effects. The achromatic doublets (two lenses) to be discussed later in this chapter, and the compound eyepieces are this kind of lens combination. A compound lens has an *equivalent focal length* (*efl*) which can be calculated from the focal length and situation of each singlet in the optical train (page 59).

3.5. *Focal length, power, aperture*

For a thin lens, the focal length f is the distance between the point where this ideal thin lens cuts the aperture and the principal focus ; the power F is the reciprocal of the focal length. The focal length f of a concave mirror is the distance of the focus from the mirror. The aperture d is the diameter of the lens or mirror, d/f is called the aperture ratio and f/d is the focal ratio. The focal plane is the plane through the principal focus, at right angles to the axis, in which the image of a small distant object lies.

The rate at which energy is collected by a lens of aperture d is proportional to d^2 ; diffraction at the aperture spreads the radiation from a distant point source over a disc in the focal plane of area proportional to $(f/d)^2$.

35

3.6. *Interference*

The oscillation of a particle* in the path of a wave of frequency ν and wavelength λ repeats itself with a period $T = 1/\nu$. If we imagine the oscillation to be timed by a clock so adjusted that the hand goes round once (turning through 2π rad) during this period T, the position of the hand indicates the *phase* of the oscillation of the particle. For two particles which are a whole wavelength apart in the path of the same wave, the phase difference is 2π ; for half a wavelength, phase difference is π ; for k wavelengths apart, phase difference is $2k\pi$; for an odd number of half-wavelengths, phase difference is $(2k+1)\pi$, where k is a whole number, or zero.

Each wave follows its own path independently of any others, and so where two sets of waves are superposed, the oscillation of each particle of the medium is such that its displacement from the mean position at any instant is the resultant of the two individual displacements. This leads to the effects called *interference* when the two waves are coherent—that is, of the same wavelength and maintaining a constant phase difference over a long time—and of the same or comparable amplitude a. If under these conditions, the waves arriving at any point differ in phase by $2k\pi$, they are in phase ' crest on crest ' and reinforce, the resultant oscillation there having amplitude $2a$, twice that of a single wave, while if the phase difference is $(2k+1)\pi$ the resultant amplitude is zero. These are the extremes, and the resultant amplitude in general lies between $2a$ and 0 at other points.

In fig. 3.9 (*a*) A and A_1 are two coherent sources, wave ' crests ' and ' troughs ' being represented by thin and thick arcs respectively. Loci of reinforcements are shown as thick fanned lines, and loci of zero amplitude as thin fanned lines ; they constitute an interference pattern.

Figure 3.9 (*b*) shows the conditions for division-of-wavefront interference, the famous ' Young's slits '. The primary slit B is narrow, and illuminated by monochromatic light ; diffraction through B gives cylindrical wave-fronts which illuminates the two slits A and A_1, and from these, two cylindrical wavefronts spread out—coherent because they come from parts of the same wavefront. A screen placed at C shows a pattern of light and dark bands parallel to the slits, giving bright maxima where they arrive in phase or $2k\pi$ out of phase, and minima where the phase difference is $(2k+1)\pi$. The object of the primary slit B is to ensure that A and A_1 emit two coherent beams. With a normal source, the inevitable fluctuations do not matter, since whatever

---

* Particles are introduced here, only to simplify the examination of wave interference.

36

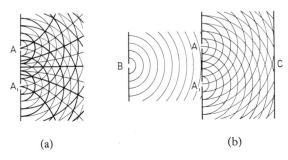

(a)   (b)

Fig. 3.9.   Interference from two light sources (division of wavefront).   (a) Interference of coherent light from two slits, (b) Young's method of producing interference from a single source.

happens before B the counting of phase differences begins only there. With a laser source, the light is itself coherent so no primary slit B is needed.

With division-of-amplitude interference, the whole wavefront is divided into two less intense whole wavefronts.   A path/phase difference between them is introduced, say by using a thin transparent film.   In fig. 3.10, where the rays normal to the wavefronts (not the wavefronts) are shown, when light strikes the upper surface of such a film, part is reflected to B at the observer's eye, part is refracted into the film to be reflected at the lower surface at C, emerging from the upper surface of the film at D to meet the observer's eye at E.   The two rays are recombined on the retina at F.   For points on the film such that the phase difference between the two recombined rays is $2k\pi$, brightness is observed ; where the phase difference is $(2k+1)\pi$, darkness.   In terms of wavelengths and path difference, this means that for a film of thickness t and refractive index n, for normal incidence, we should have brightness wherever $2nt = k\lambda$ and darkness wherever $2nt = (k+\frac{1}{2})\lambda$ if there is no phase change at the surface itself due to the reflection.

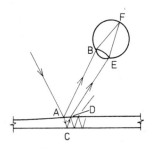

Fig. 3.10.   Thin film interference. (division of amplitude).

37

At an interface where there is optical contact a black patch appears when light waves travelling in a rarer medium (air) are reflected at the surface of a denser medium (glass). This is because there is a phase change of π. But if the denser medium comes first, no phase change takes place upon reflection. Thus where the air film is sufficiently thin for its thickness to cause to appreciable difference in the optical path lengths of the two components, then whatever the wavelength, they will have a phase difference of π and consequently zero amplitude when recombined, and no light will be reflected. Hence the observed black patch.

3.7. *Fresnel diffraction*

Huygens's construction explains (p. 30) in general terms why diffraction effects are to be expected round the edges of apertures and obstacles. We now take up some points in detail.

Dealing first with what is called Fresnel diffraction, figure 3.11 represents a plane wavefront (shown only by the edges AB) from a

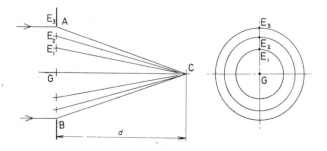

Fig. 3.11. Diffraction through a circular aperture.

distant axial point source passing through a circular aperture. All points on the wavefront are in phase at the aperture. The combined effect of the secondary wavelets at any point C will depend on where C is, because various parts of the wavefront AB are at different distances from C and so arrive there having traversed different path-lengths. Let d be the perpendicular distance from C to the wavefront. With centre C and radii $(d+\lambda/2)$, $(d+2\lambda/2)$, $(d+3\lambda/2)$ ... describe spheres which intersect the wavefront at E_1, E_2, E_3 ... The concentric circles of radius GE_1, GE_2, GE_3 ... define the inner and outer edges of the *half-period zones* for C, whose distances are such that the secondary wavelets from adjacent zones are half a wavelength (on the average) out of step with one another by the time they reach C. It can be shown that if λ is small relative to d, the area of each zone is very nearly equal to

$\pi d\lambda$, so that their contributions to C diminish only slowly. This means that if the position of C is such that the wavefront produces an even number of zones, cancellation is nearly complete and the central spot is dark, but if it produces an odd number, the odd survivor gives a central bright spot at C.

If this example is related to a slit set perpendicular to the page instead of to a circular aperture, the left hand side of fig. 3.11 is still correct but the concentric circles on the right defining the half period zones, must be replaced by a series of parallel bands of width equal to the breadth of the annuli shown, which are then called half period elements, and are not of equal area.

The result is that the image of a bright point source has an intensity distribution as fig. 3.12 (a). There is a bright central maximum, surrounded by a circular ring pattern. The radius of the first minimum, or Airy disc, in light of wavelength λ is $1\cdot22f\lambda/d$, and the least distance at which two images can be recognized as separate is when the central peak of one image falls upon the first minimum of the other (fig. 3.12 (b)). The linear resolution Δx on a photographic plate in the focal plane is thus $\Delta x = 1\cdot22f\lambda/d$, while the angular resolution $\Delta\theta = \Delta x/f = 1\cdot22\lambda/d$.

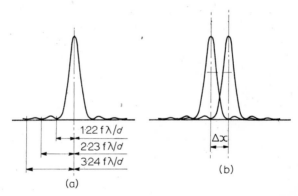

Fig. 3.12.   Light distribution in the image of a point source.   (a) The Airy disc, (b) Diffraction limit to resolving power.

3.8. *Fraunhofer diffraction : the diffraction grating*

Fraunhofer diffraction involves the use of a lens or lenses or mirrors (fig. 3.13).   Monochromatic light from a distant slit source falls as plane wavefronts upon another slit AB, parallel to the first and perpendicular to the page.   The secondary wavelets from the wavefront travelling along the axis of the lens C are brought to a focus in the focal plane at F, and reinforce there in phase since they have all traversed

39

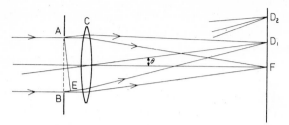

Fig. 3.13. Fraunhofer diffraction.

equal optical paths. For off-axis points D_1, D_2 . . . light from the opposite edges of the aperture traverses optical paths of different length, so we get alternating dark and light bands with increasing distance from F. A dark band occurs at D_1 if $BE = k\lambda$, and a bright one if $BE = (k + \frac{1}{2})\lambda$. The angular displacement θ from the axis is given approximately, since θ is small, by $\theta = k\lambda/w$ for a dark band and $\theta = (k + \frac{1}{2})\lambda/w$ for a bright band, where w is the width AB, and in the focal plane of the lens the linear width of the central bright band is $2\lambda f/w$. The spacing of the bands is inversely proportional to w, and with a very fine slit the diffracted light effectively spreads out to form a wide, bright, central band. This is the basis of the *diffraction grating*, for with a large number of *very fine* equally spaced parallel slits, since diffracted light which started coherently is spread in all directions, there is very strong reinforcement in just those relatively few directions in which the light from all the slits is in phase or has a constant path difference of 0, λ, 2λ, 3λ. . . . In fig. 3.14, there is a sharp bright maximum at F (path difference 0) widely spaced from adjacent maxima D_1 (first order, path difference λ), D_2 (second order, path difference 2λ). The grating interval is $(a + b)$, where a is the width of one slit and b is the width of one opaque space. For wavelength λ the angular displacement θ of the kth order reinforcement is given by $k\lambda = (a + b) \sin \theta$. The different wavelengths present in an incident beam are *dispersed* since θ depends on λ.

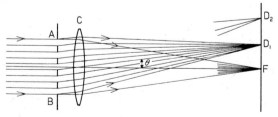

Fig. 3.14. Transmission diffraction grating.

40

The *reflection* grating has fine rulings made on a reflecting surface, which can be either plane or concave, when the focusing action of a concave mirror is added. One advantage of such a grating is that it does not absorb ultraviolet and infrared radiations, to which the glass of a transmission grating is opaque (page 128).

3.9. *Dispersion*

The separation of a pencil of light into its monochromatic components in a way that spreads them out in order of increasing or decreasing wavelength is called dispersion. The resulting pattern is a spectrum, and with a slit the spectrum consists of sharp images of the slit in every wavelength that is received from the source at the slit. A single wavelength thus gives a single line. There are :

(*a*) Continuous spectra of the light emitted from incandescent solids and liquids (and high-temperature plasma), in which every wavelength is represented ; the ideal case is that of the black body radiator.

(*b*) Line spectra arising from single atoms of elements in the gaseous state, at high temperatures or electrically excited. Each element gives its own characteristic pattern of monochromatic lines, by which it can be identified. If the gas excited to a level where its atoms are in an energy state below that from which corresponding emission occurs, is present between the slit of the spectroscope and a continuous-spectrum source, then the characteristic line spectrum of the element appears as dark lines at exactly the same positions in the spectrum as would the bright emission lines. This is an absorption line spectrum.

(*c*) Band spectra are broad bands, sharper and brighter at one edge than at the other ; the bands consist of many lines very close together ; band spectra are characteristic of molecules rather than single atoms.

It has been seen how a diffraction grating can disperse wavelengths into a spectrum. Another kind of dispersion is given by glass because the refractive index of the glass varies with wavelength. The mean refractive index n_d is that for the wavelength of the helium d line.

Colour	Hydrogen	Cadmium	Helium	Mercury
Red	C 656·3	C' 643·9		
Yellow			d 587·6	
Green				e 546·1
Blue	F 486·1	F' 480·0		g 435·8
Violet				h 404·7

Table 1. Standard reference wavelengths in nm.

41

The value of n increases as λ decreases, and the difference between the refractive index values for two wavelengths (*or* the observed linear or angular separation of these wavelengths by a prism or a lens) is called ' the dispersion ' in a general kind of way, the exact meaning being clear in the context.

The dispersion of a glass usually means the difference $(n_F - n_C)$ between the refractive indices for the red and blue lines of the emission spectrum of hydrogen, the C and F lines ; the corresponding difference for any smaller range of wavelengths is called the partial dispersion. Figure 3.15 shows the dispersions given by two prisms, one a $60°$ prism

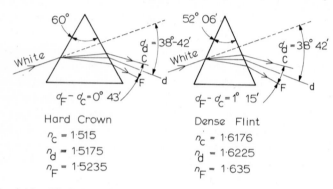

Fig. 3.15. Variation of dispersion in prisms of different glasses.

of hard crown glass, the other a $52°\ 6'$ prism of dense flint glass, the angles being chosen so that they both give the same minimum deviation for the helium d line. The angular dispersion $(d_F - d_C)$ is greater for the flint glass than for the crown glass prism. The ratio $(d_F - d_C)/d_d$ which equals $(n_F - n_C)/(n_d - 1)$ is called the dispersive power of the glass. Its reciprocal is called the constringence, symbol V.

Prisms usually give brighter spectra that diffraction gratings, because the latter spread the light out into several orders, though the rulings of reflection gratings can be shaped or ' blazed ' to concentrate light in a given wavelength. On the other hand, since $k\lambda = (a + b) \sin \theta$, all gratings give the same kind of spectrum, and the dispersion between two wavelengths depends only on k and on $(a + b)$.

Gratings have the advantage that the wavelength scale on the spectrogram is very nearly linear if the grating is mounted in the manner as described for example, for the coudé spectrograph of the 98 inch telescope in Chapter 7. This allows a wide spectrogram which covers an extensive range of wavelengths to be built up from a sequence of narrower ones, for all of which there is an acceptably linear scale.

3.10. *Aberrations*

Four main kinds of aberration are briefly described. All four affect lenses ; mirrors are exempt from chromatic aberration. All the diagrams, in this section especially, are grossly exaggerated in order to illustrate effects which are mostly very small although none the less troublesome in telescope work.

3.11. *Chromatic aberration*

A plane wavefront of white light (fig. 3.16) is incident upon a thin convex lens AB and because red light is less refracted than violet, the red is focussed farther from the lens at F_r than the violet at F_v, intermediate wavelengths being focused between these two points. Thus, a sharp violet image of the object formed at the plane of F_v will be smaller than the sharp red image formed at the plane of F_r. There is an intermediate plane CD at which the pencil has its smallest diameter and is

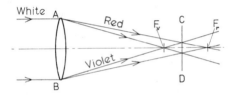

Fig. 3.16. Chromatic aberration by a biconvex lens.

composed of all the wavelengths of the original rays. A blurred, white light image of the object is formed in this plane, and this if viewed through an eye lens will be further degraded by coloured fringes arising from the difference of magnification of the sharp red and violet primary images (chromatic difference of magnification). Although the telescope primary mirror is free from chromatic aberration, some eyepieces are not and if these are used, the defect will be present.

An acceptable level of improvement for many purposes is found in a combination of two lenses which, if they are in contact, is called an achromatic doublet. Three examples are shown at fig. 3.18. The combination will focus two selected colours at a common image plane if the difference in power for the two colours in one element is cancelled by that in the other. The power of two single thin lenses in contact is equal to the sum of the separate powers and so the achromatic condition to be satisfied is that

$$F_1/V_1 = -F_2/V_2$$

43

where F is the power of the lens expressed as the reciprocal of its focal length and V is the contstringence of the respective glasses. Thus, the glasses must have different constringence values, or F_1 would equal F_2 and the doublet would have zero power. For each of the two lenses of the combination, for light of wavelength λ, the power F_λ is given by $F_\lambda = (n_\lambda - 1)(1/R_1 - 1/R_2)$ where R_1 and R_2 are the radii of curvature of the first and second surfaces respectively (the new Cartesian convention being assumed).

Careful adjustment of the curvatures of the surfaces of a doublet can also contribute to a valuable reduction in spherical aberration (fig. 3.18) which should be compared with that shown at fig. 3.17.

3.12. *Spherical aberration*

Figure 3.17 shows a plane wavefront incident upon a thin, convex lens AB. The peripheral rays focus closer to the lens, at F, than do the paraxial rays, at F^1. If a screen is placed at distance a_1 from the lens, it will show an image of a distant object point on the optical axis,

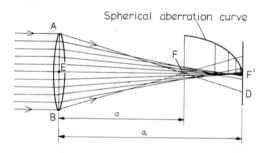

Fig. 3.17. Spherical aberration by a biconvex lens.

blurred radially to the extent F^1D. The distance $a_1 - a$ is called the longitudinal spherical aberration and the radius F^1D is called the lateral spherical aberration. If the former is known, or can be found, the latter may be expressed in the form

$$F^1D = EA \ (a_1 - a)/a_1$$

Between the focal points F and F^1 (but closer to F) there is a position at which the pencil has its smallest diameter. It is called the circle of least confusion and lies in what is then taken to be the focal plane of the lens or mirror. The aberration curve is plotted with focal length on the x axis, lateral aberration on the y axis and always takes the form shown for single, convex lenses or concave mirrors.

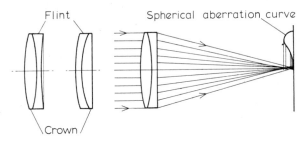

Fig. 3.18. Achromatic doublet lenses.

3.13 *Coma*

Coma is one of the image defects arising from centring errors within the telescope or from any point on the object being off the optical axis of the lens or mirror.   Figure 3.19 shows parallel rays A, B, C, D (indicating a plane wavefront) obliquely incident upon a concave mirror $E_1 F_1 G_1 H_1$.   A plane containing the optical axis of the mirror and the curved line $E_1 F_1$ is called the *tangential plane* and rays associated with it are shown as full lines.   The axial plane including the curve $G_1 H_1$ is called the *sagittal plane* and its associated rays are shown dotted.   The mirror is considered to be divided into an infinite number of annular zones typified by the concentric circles shown upon its surface.   To draw in many reflected rays from each zone would confuse the diagram, so only two tangential rays and two sagittal rays reflected from the one zone $E_1 F_1 G_1 H_1$ ('zone 1') are shown, the remainder being described but not shown.

The tangential rays from points E_1 and F_1 converge to focus at a point T_1 on the edge of a small circular patch on the image plane.   The sagittal rays from points G_1 and H_1 in the same mirror zone converge to

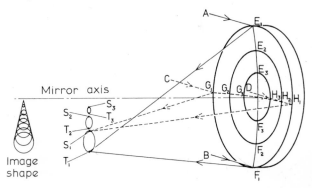

Fig. 3.19. Coma due to a concave mirror.

45

focus at point S_1 diametrically opposite to T_1 on the image patch. Together, all the rays reflected from ' zone 1 ', uniformly illuminate the circular patch. For ' zone 2 ' reflected rays from points E_2 and F_2 converge to point T_2 on the edge of a smaller image patch nearer the optical axis of the mirror, and rays from points G_2 and H_2 converge to point S_2 on this patch. Similar rays from ' zone 3 ' converge to points T_3 and S_3 on an even smaller image patch, and the combined effect of all the image patches so formed gives rise to the image shape shown.

Coma is a particularly troublesome aberration because since it is asymmetrical about all but one axis, one finds it impossible to assess where the exact centre of the image lies.

3.14. *Oblique astigmatism*

The word oblique is used with astigmatism when the latter is an aberration in a lens or mirror system, to distinguish it from the intended result produced by the use of cylindrical lenses. As in the case of coma, the defect arises when any point on the object lies off the optical axis of lens or mirror.

Figure 3.20 shows parallel rays A, B, C, D, incident obliquely upon a concave mirror EFGH. Light reflected from points E and F on the mirror, that is, in the tangential plane, (see ' Coma ' above,) is focused not as part of a point image, but as part of the horizontal line F_T the length of which is bounded by sagittal rays reflected from points G and H on the mirror. These rays from G and H converge as a part of the vertical line image F_S, the length of which is bounded by tangential rays reflected from points E and F on the mirror. The elliptical cross-sections of the pencils approaching and receding from the planes of astigmatic focus are shown hatched. Nowhere on the ray path will a sharp image of an

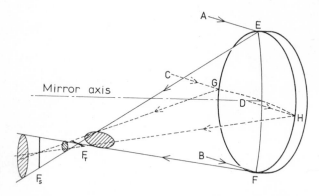

Fig. 3.20.   Oblique astigmatism due to a concave mirror.

object point be formed, but there is a plane between the tangential and sagittal focal lines where the pencil has minimum cross sectional area and this is the plane of optimum focus, shown in fig. 3.20 as a small, hatched circle.

All uncorrected lens and mirror systems suffer from oblique astigmatism, the uncorrected, defect-free field of reflecting telescopes in particular being restricted in size by this aberration, although its effect is much less than that of coma.   An improvement in the size of the prime focus and Cassegrain fields may be obtained by the use of lens correcting systems which are placed before the focal plane of the relevant mirror.

CHAPTER 4

ray paths and light losses

FIGURE 4.1. shows the ray path through the simplest kind of astronomical refracting telescope consisting of a converging objective of focal length f_1 and a converging eyepiece of shorter focal length f_2. A refractor is chosen for ease of explanation, but the principles and nomenclature apply to all telescopes.   Light from a star at the extreme edge of the field of semi-angle α, is incident upon the objective of aperture, or entrance pupil y_1.   The star image is formed on the common focal plane of objective and eyepiece.   Light diverges from the focal plane and is incident upon the eyepiece where it is refracted to a parallel

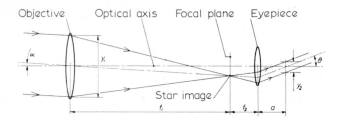

Fig. 4.1.   Ray path for a simple astronomical refracting telescope in normal (afocal) adjustment.

cylindrical pencil bounding the apparent field of semi-angle θ.   The lenses are said to be confocal when they are separated by the sum of their focal lengths, as shown, and the arrangement is then called an afocal system in which both object and secondary image are infinitely distant. The diameter of the emergent pencil, y_2, where it crosses the axis is called the exit pupil (or Ramsden circle) and the distance from this plane to the eyepiece (strictly, the final lens surface) is termed eye-relief.   The magnifying power (angular magnification) of the instrument in this adjustment may be expressed three ways :

$$m = f_1/f_2 = \tan \theta/\tan \alpha = y_1/y_2$$

Aberrations in such a telescope would be unacceptable, but light losses would be low, totalling four reflection losses, (one from each

48

surface of each lens) and a transmission loss through two thin lenses. Few instruments lose less in the visible wavelengths ; the majority lose much more. A small-field, prime-focus photograph taken with a reflecting telescope for example, will involve losses due to only one mirror reflection and a little absorption and scattering at the photographic plate. A coudé spectrogram will suffer losses from perhaps eight or more mirror and grating reflections plus slit and photoplate losses. A wide field photograph taken at the Cassegrain focus will carry the penalty of two mirror reflections, perhaps eight or more reflection losses from lens surfaces, (substantially less from Ritchey-Chrétien optics), transmission losses through many centimetres of optical glass, plus the ever-present photographic loss. All reflecting telescopes suffer a loss arising from the shadow cast upon the primary mirror by equipment mounted at or near the prime focus, in the focal plane of the primary mirror.

Because most modern telescopes are large, and the size excludes *dioptric* instruments (the refractors, in which all the optical elements are lenses), we shall describe only *catoptric* instruments, in which the principal elements are mirrors, and *catadioptric* instruments which combine the best characteristics of lenses and mirrors.

4.1. *The Newtonian reflector*

Figure 4.2 shows the Newtonian reflector in which the diagonal flat mirror intercepts the reflected rays from the paraboloidal primary mirror and directs them out through the side of the telescope tube where the primary image may be examined conveniently by the eyepiece. It lost popularity when telescopes developed to a size which rendered the position of the eyepiece inconveniently high above the observing floor, but on smaller instruments, the diagonal flat and the eyepiece may be mounted in a common assembly which is rotatable about the telescope tube axis, an arrangement which allows the eyepiece to be brought to a convenient, horizontal attitude, whatever the attitude of the telescope.

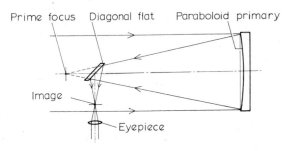

Fig. 4.2. Ray path for a Newtonian telescope.

4.2. *The Gregorian reflector*

Figure 4.3 shows Gregory's variation of Newton's arrangement. The paraboloidal primary mirror remains but the diagonal flat is replaced by a concave ellipsoidal secondary mirror placed beyond the plane of prime focus, which reflects rays from the primary to form an image field centred upon the optical axis of the telescope. Images so formed are viewed through a central hole in the primary mirror with an eyepiece on the optical axis. It has the possible advantage that the observer looks towards the object, while with the Newtonian the object is always 90° from the line of sight. Used only in certain highly specialized applications today (see Chapter 10) the Gregorian lacked popularity due to the difficulty of manufacturing the concave ellipsoidal secondary. Excessive tube length and hence the size of the dome is the modern objection.

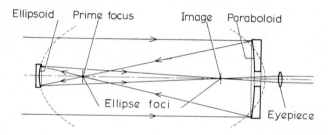

Fig. 4.3. Ray path for a Gregorian telescope.

4.3. *The Cassegrain reflector*

Figure 4.4. shows Cassegrain's variation. The perforated paraboloid primary mirror remains, but the ellipsoidal secondary is replaced by a convex hyperboloid placed inside the plane of prime focus, which gives a shorter tube. The image is formed behind the primary mirror, the rays passing through the hole in its centre, and is viewed with an eyepiece

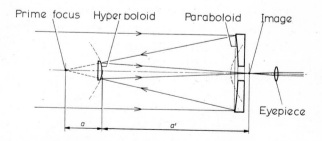

Fig. 4.4. Ray path for a Cassegrain telescope.

on the optical axis. It is an extremely popular configuration and all the world's largest and most modern telescopes include this facility. In order to change the size of the primary image in a reflecting telescope it would be necessary to change the primary mirror for one of different focal length—which is unthinkable, but magnification at the Cassegrain focus may be, and frequently is, varied by changing the smaller secondary mirror. The ratio a'/a in fig. 4.4 defines the magnification of the secondary image which may be further increased by use of an appropriate eyepiece.

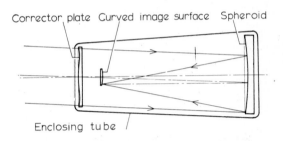

Fig. 4.5. Ray path for a Schmidt camera.

4.4. *The Schmidt camera*

Figure 4.5 is more accurately described as a camera, for its sole function until recently has been photographic. The Schmidt overcomes a problem which is inherent in all telescopes, especially reflectors, and that is, limitation of the field of view due to a rapid deterioration in quality of images which are only a little way from the optical axis of the telescope. The best and most fully corrected large telescopes handle a field semi-angle little more than about twenty arc minutes without deterioration in image quality, but the Schmidt camera extends this field to four or five degrees. The original instrument built by Bernard Schmidt in 1930 was of 14 inch aperture and accepted a field semi-angle of 8°. This value is reduced in larger instruments, but even one of the world's largest, the 48 inch Schmidt camera of the Palomar Observatory, covers a field semi-angle of three degrees. The Schmidt camera uses a concave spheroidal primary mirror, at the centre of curvature of which is located a corrector plate, a lens-like optical element which is flat on the rear surface and figured to a complex computed profile on the front surface. The field is focused upon a spherically curved surface and the photographic plates therefore have to be controlled to this shape.

The diagram shows incident light from a star, purposely shown at the

51

edge of the field to illustrate that the diameter of the mirror needs to be greater than that of the corrector plate. This gives rise to a special way of specifying the Schmidt camera which is said to be an $a : b : c :$ instrument where a and b are the apertures of the corrector plate and primary mirror respectively and c is the focal length of the mirror. Very 'fast' optics result, for mirrors of low focal ratio can be used in conjunction with the corrector plate, which allows for a tidy compact design, invariably contained in a closed tube.

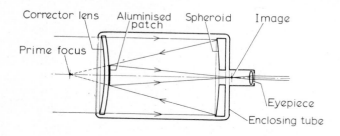

Fig. 4.6.   Ray path for a Maksutov telescope.

4.5. *The Maksutov reflector*

Figure 4.6 shows the Cassegrain variant of the Maksutov arrangement and represents a very high level of telescope development. All four optical surfaces (two transmitting and two reflecting are spherical and in the version shown the secondary mirror is simply an aluminized patch deposited upon the rear surface of the corrector lens, which obviates the need for a supporting spider. The image is cast through the perforated primary and viewed on-axis through an eyepiece. A wider field of view is obtained with the Maksutov than with catoptric telescopes and the corrector allows the use of a very 'fast' primary. Because the vertex of the corrector is inside the focus of the primary mirror an extremely compact telescope results, always housed in an enclosing tube. Although near to perfection, the Maksutov can never challenge the status of the big reflectors, for since it is a catadioptric instrument its size is limited by the maximum practical aperture of the unsupported corrector lens. For a given aperture, the Maksutov outclasses all kinds of telescope in almost every respect. An expertly designed instrument is practically free from spherical aberration, coma and astigmatism, and may be arranged to produce a bright image on a wide flat field from a telescope of which the tube length may be as short as one fifth of the equivalent focal length of the system.

52

4.6. *Variations*

Solutions appear from time to time, to ease the problems of manufacturing large, aspheric optical surfaces or to improve telescope performance. Two variations applied to the basic Cassegrain telescope are particularly worthy of note. The Dall-Kirkham variation comprises a concave, ellipsoidal primary and a convex spherical secondary. With only one aspheric mirror surface required, manufacture is less difficult, so tending to a better image on the optical axis than the classical Cassegrain, but coma from oblique incidence is more than three times as great for typical telescope geometry.

The Ritchey-Chrétien solution has universal approval among modern telescope designers for its high quality performance, although mirror-making difficulties abound. It is an arrangement for which spherical aberration *and coma* are corrected at the Cassegrain focus. This can be achieved if correction of spherical aberration at the primary focus of the classical Cassegrain telescope is abandoned. To secure the elimination of coma, the instrument must be aplanatic. This is a term given to a system in which, if spherical aberration is corrected, coma for object points close to the axis will be eliminated when $\sin u / \sin u'$ is constant for every zone of the mirrors, (see fig. 3.19 p. 45) where u and u' are the semi-angles of the mirror zones subtended at the object and image points respectively. This expression derives from the Abbe sine condition for lenses,

$$\sin u / \sin u' = m \ (n'/n).$$

The R–Ch solution achieves this end by using a primary mirror which has a hyperbolic profile, in conjunction with a larger departure from classical form at the secondary mirror. The solution eliminates the most serious defect of the classical telescope, especially for the lower focal ratios, typically about $f/8$ at the Cassegrain focus in the modern instrument. There are other forms of aplanatic instrument, but the R–Ch has the great merit of a short tube length, the value of which will be shown in Chapter 5.

4.7. *Correctors*

Every reflecting telescope designed and built to perfection (if that were possible) would produce an image of a star in the exact centre of a curved field, of a quality governed only by the diffraction limit of the instrument and the seeing conditions as they arise. Departure from the central image position brings astigmatism to the R–Ch solution, plus coma in the Cassegrain telescope. Both defects get worse the nearer the image is to the edge of the field and the lower is the focal ratio. Hence they are very troublesome indeed at the prime focus, typically about $f/3$ in a modern instrument and remain quite unacceptable at the Cassegrain focus, about $f/8$. At the coudé focus, about $f/30$, the effects are minimal for the classical telescope, but coma difficulties remain for the R–Ch solution. To remedy matters at the two short-focus observing stations, dioptric elements are introduced into the optical train, the oldest form of which is the field-flattening lens which may also contribute a useful reduction in astigmatism if it is placed just inside the image plane. Immediately a lens is introduced in an otherwise reflective system, chromatic aberration arises and further optical glassware is required for its correction.

Figures 4.7 and 4.8 show how effectively this problem can be dealt with. They also show the vital part that computers play in modern telescope design for they are spot diagrams at the secondary (R–Ch) focus of the 3·6 m instrument of the European Southern Observatory, a telescope which is still being built at the time of writing (see Chapter 11). The diagrams were kindly provided by Carl Zeiss, Oberkochen, with the approval of ESO and show the plotted results from computer-

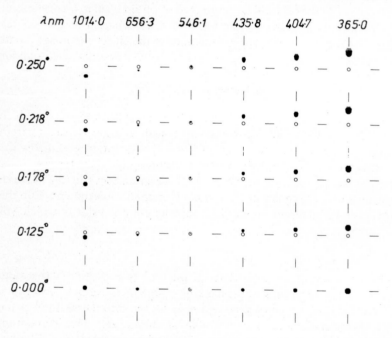

Fig. 4.7. Spot diagram for the Ritchey–Chrétien (R–Ch) focus, with singlet corrector. 3·5 m telescope of the European Southern Observatory. (ESO). *Carl Zeiss, Oberkochen.*

calculated co-ordinates at the focal plane, of 120 separate parallel, monochromatic rays, uniformly distributed and incident upon the primary mirror, at the angles of inclination to the optical axis shown in the left hand column. Wavelength in nm heads each column and each small circle is 0·18 arc second in diameter (measured from the location of the primary mirror) and is centred upon the theoretical position of a point image according to geometric optics. The designed field semi-angle is 15 minutes of arc. Figure 4.7 shows spot diagrams resulting from the application of a singlet corrector and fig. 4.8 shows similar diagrams using a doublet corrector. The improvement due to the presence of the second element is practically complete.

Similar improvement at the short-focus, primary image plane is much more difficult to achieve and fig. 4.9* gives evidence of this, being the detail of the original plate corrector for the same telescope, the upper part of the diagram showing its position relative to the primary mirror.

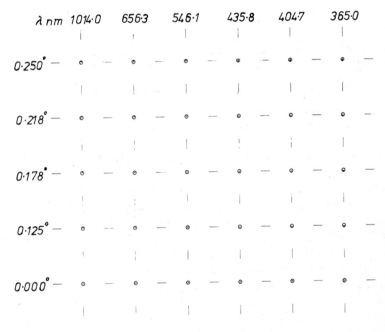

Fig. 4.8.   Spot diagram for the R–Ch focus, with doublet corrector.   3·5 m telescope of the European Southern Observatory.   (ESO).   *Carl Zeiss, Oberkochen.*

* Figure 4.9 gives the ESO primary as 3500 mm aperture because Carl Zeiss worked to this specification before the blank, which turned out at 3600 mm, was made.

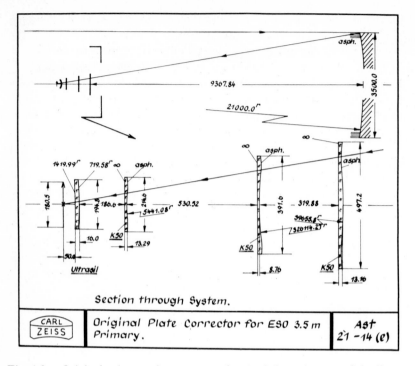

Fig. 4.9. Original primary plate corrector for the 3·5 m telescope of the European Southern Observatory (ESO). *Carl Zeiss, Oberkochen.*

Four elements involving two spherical, three aspheric and three plane
surfaces, and more than 50 mm central thickness of glass, are very costly
in both money and light losses as we shall later see.   This optical train
has since been modified to three aspheric plates of improved performance.   Three spherical lenses giving equivalent correction are planned,
but either scheme underlines the complexities of prime focus correction.

The Dall-Kirkham solution mentioned earlier, suffers pronounced
coma at the field edge in order that the secondary mirror may be simplified and to recover image fidelity, complex correction must be applied,
even at the secondary focus.   Figure 4.10 shows a schematic arrangement of a 3·5 m D–K instrument corrected for a field semi-angle of 15
minutes of arc.   The corrector consists of three lenses, all with spherical
surfaces, and one which is plane on the incident face and weakly aspheric
on the other.   The central glass thickness totals about 120 mm.

4.8 *The human eye ; an outline of its behaviour*

Figure 4.11 shows a horizontal section of the right eye.   The eyeball

56

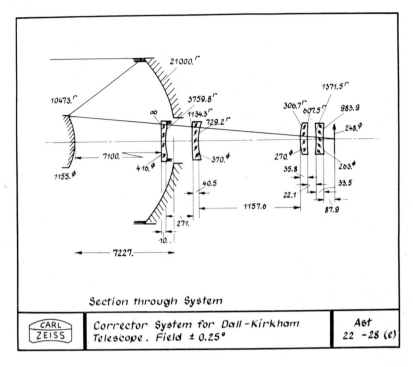

Section through System

| CARL ZEISS | Corrector System for Dall-Kirkham Telescope. Field ± 0.25° | Ast 22 -28 (e) |

Fig. 4.10. Corrector for a 3·5 m Dall-Kirkham telescope. *Carl Zeiss, Oberkochen.*

is formed mainly by the sclera, S, a tough, opaque casing. The aperture region is contained behind the cornea C, a transparent envelope forming the principal refracting surface. The crystalline lens L, curiously named for it has the texture of soft gristle, is centred by the suspensory ligaments SL which in turn attach to the annular ciliary muscle, CM. In front of the lens is the iris diaphragm, I, controlling the size of the aperture, A. The space between cornea and lens is filled with a transparent fluid called aqueous humour. The interior of the eye is lined with the light sensitive retina, R, which is separated from the sclera by the choroid, Ch, a pigmented, light absorbing layer which also contains the vital blood vessels. Very near to the intersection of the optic axis and the retina is a small area termed the macula lutea, ML, (the yellow spot) having at its centre a tiny depression, the fovea centralis, which is the most discriminating part of the retina in daylight. The retina is formed from a mass of nerve endings, the fibres of which exit from the eye as the optic nerve, ON, giving rise to the blind spot at this point.

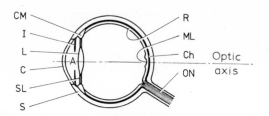

Fig. 4.11. Transverse section through an eye.

The cavity encompassed by the retina is filled with a transparent jelly called vitreous humour.

With the eye focused on a distant object, the ciliary muscle is relaxed. The suspensory ligaments radially tension the lens and adjust its curvature and axial position. When the object is brought near to the eye, annular contraction of the ciliary muscle reduces the tension in the suspensory ligaments which shifts the axial position of the lens and allows its natural elasticity to increase its surface curvatures, so maintaining the image in focus upon the retina. The iris is an involuntary device which adjusts the aperture according to the quantity of light entering the eye. It is controlled to between about two and four millimetres diameter in daylight, and about eight millimetres diameter in complete darkness.

The nerve endings comprising the retina are of two kinds ; they are approximately shaped to the form of either rods or cones. Rods are very sensitive to light intensity but contribute nothing to colour perception. They contain a photochemical compound called visual purple which assumes that colour after a period of twenty to forty minutes in darkness, and results in the eye attaining maximum sensitivity to minimal light levels. The eye is then said to be dark-adapted, but in this condition, exposure to bright light for a very short time bleaches the visual purple and the eye reverts to normal daylight sensitivity. Rods are most abundant at the retinal periphery, reducing in numbers towards the fovea which is composed almost entirely of cones. The latter are exclusively responsible for colour perception and are much less sensitive to light level. They are also very much smaller in diameter in the foveal region than elsewhere on the retina, corresponding approximately to the minimum resolvable image size fixed by the diffraction limit (see Chapter 3) of the eye in normal daylight ; a good example of nature's economy.

The foregoing explains, in the simplest manner, why visual acuity is best in daylight where light levels are intense enough to excite the smallest cones, so stimulating perception of colour and fine detail. It also explains why after dark, colourless vision persists and maximum

58

acuity is achieved by looking slightly to one side of the object so that its image does not fall upon the concentration of less sensitive cones at the fovea. The remarkable organization of these facilities provides us with vision over a range of about ten million to one in relative luminance per unit area of the object.

4.9. *Eyepieces*

Figure 4.1 shows how telescope magnification depends on the focal length of the eyepiece, but this latter is depicted as a single thin lens, while many eyepieces consist of at least two lenses, a field lens and an eye lens. The simple calculation of magnifying power works if we use the *equivalent focal length* (*efl*) for the compound eyepiece. Figure 4.12 shows such an eyepiece, with the field lens receiving a pencil of parallel

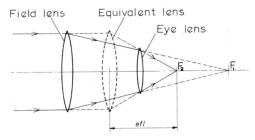

Fig. 4.12.   Equivalent focal length of an eyepiece.

monochromatic light. The refracted rays would normally converge to a focus at F_1, at distance f_1 from the field lens, but for the presence of the eye lens which intercepts the converging beam and further refracts it to focus at F_2. If the incident rays are produced past the field lens, and the twice refracted rays are produced back past the eye lens they will intersect upon a plane at a distance from F_2 which is the *efl* of the compound eyepiece. A single thin equivalent lens (shown dotted) of focal length = *efl* placed at this plane will perform for magnifying purposes exactly as the compound eyepiece does. The *efl* for any two adjacent lenses is expressed as

$$efl = f_1 \times f_2/(f_1 + f_2 - d)$$

where f_1, f_2 are the focal lengths of the field lens and the eye lens and d is their separation. Complex systems may be analysed by the extension of this process.

Eyepieces deserve a whole book to themselves, but here we need consider only two matters, the contribution to the telescope's magnifying power and the size of the exit pupil. The diffraction limit to the resolving power is inversely proportional to the aperture of the objective and it is pointless to use an eyepiece of higher magnifying power than that which exhausts the resolving power of the telescope. For example, the aperture of a 2 m telescope is about 250 times larger than that of a dark-adapted eye, so an eyepiece giving an angular magnification greater than 250 reveals no additional detail, and serves only to aggravate the degrading effects of atmospheric ' seeing '. It is also very desirable to use an eyepiece which has an exit pupil which approximates in size to the aperture of the observer's eye. If the exit pupil is larger than this, the iris of the eye excludes a proportion of the light collected by the telescope primary mirror, so the same image brightness could have been obtained with an objective of smaller aperture. If the exit pupil is smaller than the aperture of the eye, the full capacity of the dark-adapted eye is not exploited. Closely associated with this aspect is eye relief, (see fig. 4.1), for the observer's eye must be located on the plane of the Ramsden circle for optimum performance. Thus, if he is not obliged to wear spectacles at the telescope, he may select an eyepiece with an eye relief as short as 3 or 4 mm, but if spectacles are needed, eye-relief of 10 to 12 mm is a desirable minimum. There are more than sixty different eyepieces designed for telescope use, and all act for magnifying purposes like the single thin lens of fig. 4.1

4.10 *The Huygenian eyepiece*

The most common form of the Huygens eyepiece uses two plano-convex lenses, the plane surfaces facing the eye as in fig. 4.13 (*a*). Its merits are simplicity, fairly wide angular field and complete freedom from distortion and troublesome internal reflections. It has minimal chromatic difference of magnification and fairly good eye relief if the designed equivalent focal length is not too short. It is unsuitable for measuring purposes because the focal plane lies between the lenses. A further restriction is spherical aberration which begins to get troublesome on telescopes with focal ratio less than about $f/9$, making it more suitable for refractors than reflectors. It is however, widely used with reflectors at the Cassegrain focus. The defects are minimized when the ratio of focal lengths of field and eye lens is between 2 : 1 and 3 : 1 and the lens separation is half the sum of the focal lengths.

4.11. *The Ramsden eyepiece*

The Ramsden eyepiece shown at fig. 4.13 (*b*) is even simpler than the Huygenian, consisting of two plano-convex lenses which may be identical, convex surfaces facing, and no internal diaphragm. It has a similar field angle to the Huygenian, the field is a little flatter, but chromatic

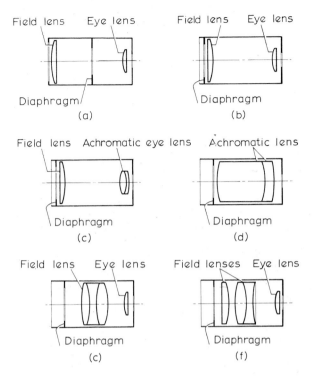

Fig. 4.13. Eyepieces in general use. (a) Huygenian, (b) Ramsden, (c) Kellner, (d) Solid, (e) Orthoscopic, (f) Wide angle.

difference of magnification is strongly evident at the periphery. Spherical aberration is less than with the Huygenian, but so is eye relief. Aberrations are minimized when each lens lies on the focal plane of the other, but this brings any dust on the field lens into sharp focus and it is common practice to reduce the lens separation a little to obviate this nuisance. It also suffers a little from ' ghost ' images reflected from the convex surfaces.

4.12. *The Kellner eyepiece*

The Kellner eyepiece shown at fig. 4.13 (*c*) is, in effect, an achromatic Ramsden in which the singlet eye lens is replaced by an achromatic doublet. This minimizes the chromatic difficulties evident at the edge of the field in the Ramsden and when expertly designed, it can also contribute to a further reduction in the small amount of spherical aberration. In the lower powers, this eyepiece is excellent.

4.13. *The solid eyepiece*

Figure 4.13 (*d*) typifies a solid eyepiece of which there are many types. The two main ones are the Tolles which is a single piece of glass ground as a thick lens, and the Hastings variant in which a second element is cemented to the first, providing improved chromatic correction. Two further types are the Coddington and Stanhope magnifiers. All provide very sharp definition near the field centre, they have little or no internal reflections and correct reasonably well for spherical and chromatic abberation. For a given total thickness of glass, they lose less light than multi-lens eyepieces because there are fewer reflecting surfaces.

4.14. *The orthoscopic eyepiece*

Orthoscopic eyepieces vary in design, all being multi-lens systems. Figure 4.13 (*e*) shows a variation using a combination of a triplet field lens and a singlet eye lens whilst other forms employ two similar cemented doublets. These types have possibly the highest aggregate of advantages in the general purpose range, including up to 50° apparent field, and good eye-relief, which make them popular with spectacle wearers.

4.15. *The wide angle eyepiece*

The modern wide angle eyepiece shown at fig. 4.13 (*f*) characterizes a family of eyepieces which achieve very wide apparent field angles by the use of as many as five or six lenses. Two such eyepieces which have gained popularity are the Erfle and the Bertele with apparent field angles of 68° and 70° respectively. As one might expect, some oblique astigmatism is evident at the edge of such a wide field, but for such work as star field sweeps and comet tail oberservations, these eyepieces have some advantages. They are also designed for optimum performance in conjunction with the modern telescope of low focal ratio which distinguishes them from the others reviewed above which, while being very useful down the scale, do not exploit their maximum potential on instruments of less than about $f/15$, or in the case of the orthoscopic about $f/10$.

We can now consider all the radiation losses encountered from star to observer. The term ' radiation ' is used rather than ' light ' because the range of wavelengths involved extends well beyond the range (about 380 nm to 760 nm) of the visible spectrum.

4.16. *Losses in space and atmosphere*

All telescopes will, without special provision, focus a bandwidth extending a little beyond the visible and reflectors in particular are capable of focusing a vastly extended spectrum if all the optical elements in the ray path are reflective. This is an advantage in the infrared region of the spectrum but of reduced value in ground-based telescopes in the ultraviolet region for reasons which will be mentioned presently.

Radiation from a distant star will encounter many hazards before arriving in a ground-based observatory. Vast clouds of gas, dust and cosmic debris swarm in space ready to impede all but the radiofrequency emissions with which this book is not concerned. An edge-on view of almost any spiral galaxy, for example NGC 4565 in Coma Berenices shown in fig. 4.14, illustrates very well the obscuring material present in

Fig. 4.14. Obscuring material in NGC 4565, in Coma Berenices. *Science Museum, London.* By courtesy of Mount Wilson Observatory.

the galactic plane. Within our own galaxy, two of the most prominent of these dark nebulae are the Horse's Head in Orion and the Coal Sack in the Southern Cross, each, among many others, representing huge screens, impenetrable to visible light, in the night sky. The bright nebulae which absorb light at some wavelengths and emit it at other wavelengths are almost as troublesome. The gas cloud around the stars forming the sword of Orion is one such obstacle of considerable beauty, as seen through a small telescope.

Ultraviolet radiation from the stars is largely absorbed in physical processes in the atmosphere. Prominent among these effects is the conversion of oxygen, at mesospheric altitude (30 to 80 km) into ozone, which itself absorbs ultra-violet radiation and so serves as a protective shield preventing this from reaching the surface.

There are many more atmospheric effects which absorb or attenuate energy on its way to the observatory. It can be seen that blue light is substantially attenuated, for it is scattered from sunlight to provide the blue of the sky. The red appearance of the sun at sunset, when its radiation reaches the observer horizontally and so traverses the maximum atmospheric path length, is complementary to the blue sky, and shows further the selective filtering effect of great distances of air upon the shorter-wavelength components of the visible spectrum (fig. 4.15).

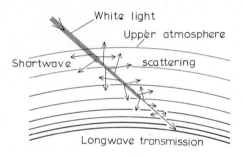

Fig. 4.15. Light scattering in the atmosphere.

Water vapour very seriously impedes transmission of infrared radiation, and condensed as water droplets into cloud or mist will stop any direct visible rays, allowing only transmission of scattered and attentuated light. The elements of the atmosphere also absorb selectivity. Air is composed of nitrogen and oxygen in the ratio of about 4 : 1, a little carbon dioxide, and traces of the noble gases and some gaseous compounds ; add to this the high-altitude ozone, a few man-made pollutants and some natural suspensions, and the filtering effect of the atmosphere is quite considerable !

William Wollaston, in 1802, discovered dark absorption lines crossing the solar spectrum. While measuring the refractive index of optical glasses, Joseph Fraunhofer further studied them and in 1815 he catalogued the positions of 576 dark lines crossing the continuous spectrum. More than 25 000 are catalogued today. G. G. Kirchhoff and R. W. Bunsen in 1860 gave an explanation of the dark Fraunhofer lines. They showed that both bright and dark lines occupied (separately of course) identical precisely defined positions in the continuous spectrum. It was later determined that bright lines are due to light emission by atoms which have been excited to high energy levels, while dark lines are produced by the absorption of the same discrete wavelengths by atoms of the same element at lower energy levels.

The Earth's atmosphere produces its own dark absorption lines on the spectrogram of the star. These are now recognized as telluric lines, but they gave early astrophysicists endless trouble because the dark-line ' fingerprints ' (each pattern of lines being unique to a given element) were attributed to the cooler outer shells of the stars when in fact they were caused by the terrestrial environment.

Figure 4.16 illustrates the spectral transmission characteristics, greatly simplified, of the Earth's atmosphere at sea level. Over the enormous wavelength bandwidth 10 km to 10^{-2} pm there are only two significantly transparent regions (' windows ') in an otherwise opaque blanket. Of these windows, the wider one, transparent only to radio emission within the bandwidth 10 m to 1 mm, does not concern the present book, which is interested mainly in what comes through the optical window, transparent only to radiation between about 290 nm and 1050 nm, so long as we remain ground-based. The diagram shows wavelength in logarithmically decreasing order from left to right. Below the wavelength scale is shown the position of the ' windows ', with atmospheric attenuating factors marked. At the bottom is shown a range of detectors available to the telescope observer for a range of wavelengths but it must be stressed that while the telescope remains ground-based it will only receive radiation through the optical window. To extend the detectable bandwidth to the frontiers of the microwaves at the red end and into the X-rays at the violet end would necessitate taking the telescope above the Earth's atmosphere and into orbit, which in fact will be discussed in Chapter 10.

Less predictable are the losses due to particulate suspensions of solid and liquid material in the air, ranging from sheets of ice crystals in the upper atmosphere, through cloud formations lower down, to dust suspensions only a few kilometres overhead. The latter may be due to natural causes like the residue from sand and dust storms in some parts of the world or to industrial activity in others. Either way, the atmospheric circulation takes some of this airborne material into the line of sight of the telescope at some time and because of its particle size, far larger than any gas molecule, it does not absorb in a spectrally selective way and will scatter light of all wavelengths in all directions, reducing the luminance observed at the telescope.

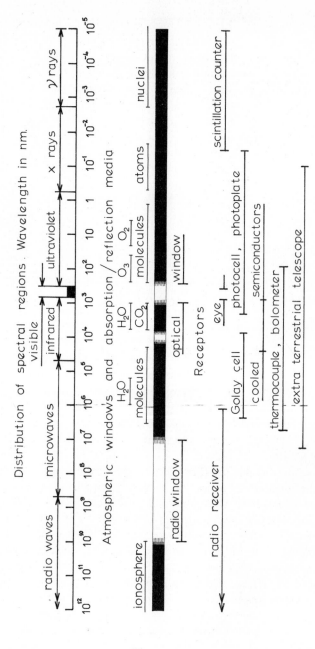

Fig. 4.16. The electromagnetic spectrum.

4.17. *Seeing*

Worrying though light losses may be, distortions and spurious image displacements are far more troublesome and they are present all the time to a varying and mostly unpredictable extent. When a light ray arrives at the Earth's atmosphere from its star source it will, for our purposes, have completed the interstellar journey in a straight line. It will not continue its rectilinear journey uninterrupted to the telescope objective, even though it is of the right wavelength to penetrate the optical window. The final stage is through a few kilometres of air which increases in density, pressure and temperature as the penetration proceeds ; and natural processes keep this gaseous ocean continuously stirred. The refractive index of air depends on the air temperature and density for a given wavelength. Refractive index will therefore increase for a given wavelength as the ground is approached. This increase is systematic and therefore predictable, and all would be well but for the superposed effects due to random and unpredictable turbulence and thermal instability. These random effects contribute *lateral* fluctuations in refractive index, often oscillating with frequency up to 100 Hz, and extending to great heights. The overall result is to produce transient changes in the refractive index of the air, fluctuating with a random frequency. Air in this quite normal state may be regarded as a highly unstable and unwelcome extension to the telescope ; it intercepts the plane wave-fronts from a distant star, so essential to perfect image formation and, tens of kilometres in front of the instrument, irreversibly distorts and corrugates it (fig. 4.17). Possibly the most common and certainly the most troublesome effect (to the astronomer) arises from turbulent ripples of refractive index in the line of sight which are comparable to or even smaller in distribution than the linear aperture of the large telescope. The corresponding familiar naked-eye phenomenon of scintillation is popularly called twinkling.

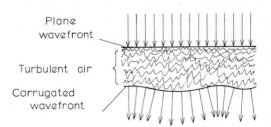

Fig. 4.17. Wavefront corrugation by the atmosphere, the principal cause of poor seeing.

Scintillation is more pronounced near the horizon than elsewhere and the reason for this is that starlight arriving at the observer horizontally traverses a far greater distance in turbulent air than at higher angles of elevation and so suffers far more deviations and chromatic dispersions. Not so obvious to the naked eye is the difference between two kinds of scintillation, brightness and chromatic. It is fairly easy, with the unaided eye and a little practice, to pick out planets from stars due to the relatively steady light appearance of the former, and the scintillating appearance of the latter. An interesting phenomenon produces this difference, for if a light source (and for this purpose, both planets and stars are regarded as sources) is observed through the atmosphere with an instrument of small aperture, an eye for example, it will show rapid changes of intensity called brightness scintillation and the amplitude of the scintillation increases with diminishing apparent diameter of the source. Hence, since all the known planets (the Moon is the limiting case) have finite apparent discs, which diminish with increasing distance, they all scintillate less than the stars, the largest of which is still too far distant to be resolved into a disc by the largest telescope at present available.

Chromatic scintillation of the object is an apparent fluctuating change of colour, and is caused by chromatic dispersion effects arising from atmospheric disturbances which first disperse the star's radiation into a spectrum and then proceed to make the spectrum oscillate across the aperture of the receiving instrument. If the aperture is small, (as in the case of one's eye, binoculars, or a small telescope) the spectral components will be seen separately, giving rise to a coloured twinkle. But if the aperture is large enough to receive the dispersed spectrum complete, it behaves as an integrating device, recombining all the spectral components at the focal plane to form a blurred image, because the incident wavefront has been corrugated by the atmosphere and only plane wavefronts produce sharp images in the focal plane.

Thus, the troublesome scintillations are caused either by refraction and dispersion due to transient lens and prism effects in the air, or by diffraction as light passes the somewhat ill-defined edges of the small cells of air which, due to temperature and density differences of neighbouring cells, form such lenses and prisms. The overall effect is to produce not a single star image of definite diameter which is limited only by the diffraction limit of the telescope aperture, but a whole swarm of images in a matter of a fraction of a second, the swarm diameter being larger than that of the diffraction-limited image by a factor of, say, twenty to several hundred, depending upon the size of the telescope. The integration time required by the fastest photo-emulsion does not normally allow these separate scintillation images to be photographed at all, which makes the evidence shown in fig. 4.18 the more remarkable. Twelve photographs of the bright star Aldebaran are displayed. They were taken at the Observatoire du Pic-du-Midi using the Lallemand electronic camera in conjunction with the 1 m telescope. Electronic amplification of the signal available enabled these frames to be exposed at 25 ms intervals for a period of 2 ms each frame. The small dot at the head of the arrow on the top right-hand frame indicates the approximate true size of a diffraction-limited star image through the same telescope. It is analogous to the clean, small hole produced in a target by a single bullet, relative to the mess produced by firing a shotgun at the same spot, and the integration of many images so degraded is termed a shimmer disc.

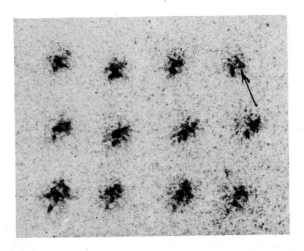

Fig. 4.18. Scintillation of the star Aldebaran. Each frame, taken at 25 ms intervals, was exposed for 2 ms using the Lallemand electronic camera. *Observatoire du Pic-du-Midi.*

To the visual observer, scintillation is apparent and the shimmer disc is not, while on the normal photographic plate, the reverse is the case. This is due to the very short duration of visual persistence at low light levels, so that stimulation of the retina from one scintillation decays before the next produces a new, displaced image ; whilst the photograph sums the total of images forming the shimmer disc over a period which may extend to several hours of exposure time. It explains why there is still scope for visual astronomy in an age where the camera is taking over an increasing amount of observing time, for the atmospheric conditions in the line of sight at any instant govern the quality of the ' seeing ' at that instant.   There are periods at every location, sometimes just fleeting moments, when the ' seeing ' is by the laws of probability, exceptionally good and then the experienced visual observer can see far more detail than the camera can record, which is why many planet observers prefer to draw an art impression of their own findings rather than abdicate to the camera, which cannot discriminate between good seeing and bad.

It has become customary of recent years, to site large observatories at places where the seeing is known to be predominantly good, and where the scintillation frequency drops from something like 100 Hz to as low as 1 to 10 Hz with a corresponding reduction of shimmer disc size.   Such observatories are all sited at high altitude and below regions of the atmosphere known to be optically quiescent, of exceptional purity and very dry.   Having traversed both space and atmosphere, the light rays enter the observatory where further losses are inevitable but much more predictable.

Telescopes, correctors and eyepieces have been examined earlier and it remains to analyse the losses arising from the optical elements involved.

4.18. *Instrument losses*

The early reflecting telescopes equipped with speculum-metal mirrors suffered loss of about 45 per cent of the incident light when the metal was freshly polished, with further loss as the easily tarnished surface dimmed.   This did not matter a great deal to the observer since vision, like most other senses, is logarithmic in sensitivity and up to 70 per cent of the light may be lost without serious change in stimulus.   But, the photographic plate is roughly linear in sensitivity and loss of light has to be paid for in exposure time.   Chemically applied silver coating on glass improved mirror performance and reduced losses to as little as 5 to 7 per cent in the visible wavelengths when the coating was new; but this fell rapidly and severely as the surface tarnished, mainly as a result of traces of sulphur compounds in the atmosphere.

Almost without exception, the modern telescope uses mirrors coated by evaporation with a very thin film of aluminium.   The aluminizing process takes place in a vacuum chamber evacuated to a pressure of < 0.007 pascal.   The film is controlled to a thickness of about half a wavelength of yellow light and a reflecting surface as flawless as the optically worked glass beneath the film results.   In new condition such a surface loses a little more than 10 per cent of incident light in the visible wavelengths, and a further 2 per cent in the ultraviolet down to 250 nm ;

but it improves steadily in the infrared from 9 per cent loss at 1000 nm wavelength to a mere 1 per cent at 50 000 nm.

Aluminium is very quick to oxidize, and within hours of removal from the vacuum chamber, a thin film of durable aluminium oxide is formed on the surface which does little to reduce its reflecting properties. The passage of time, however, does cause some deterioration which may be delayed by adequate conditioning of the air fed to the mirror cell. A primary mirror so cared for will require washing at three- to six-monthly intervals and re-aluminizing every year or two, during which period the reflection loss in the visible is likely to increase to more than 15 per cent.

The exception mentioned above, is the most modern of techniques for the control of reflection, multi-layer coating, which uses thin-film interference. Light reflected from or transmitted through as many as thirty separate films, which are carefully applied and controlled for thickness, can achieve very high, or very low levels of reflection at a given wavelength, as required.

In 1967 work was started at the Dominion Astrophysical Observatory,

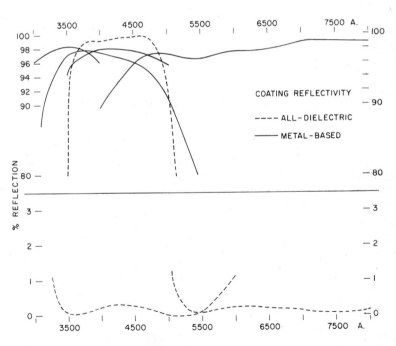

Fig. 4.19. Reflectance values for multilayer dielectric and conducting coatings. *Dominion Astrophysical Observatory, Victoria, B.C.*

Victoria, British Columbia, on the development of an efficient coudé spectrograph system involving multilayer-coated elements (fig. 4.19). The upper curves refer to mirrors and the lower to lens surfaces, which we shall discuss presently. Of the upper curves, one curious effect arising from the application of the all-dielectric coating (dotted line) may be seen in fig. 5.6, page 81. The rectangular glass flat in the upper half of the picture is coated in this way, and the red crayon writing upon it is actually on the back of the glass, which shows that there is strong transmission at wavelengths reflected by the crayon colour ; yet this flat is a mirror almost 100 per cent reflecting to blue light on the facing side. Hold the picture up to a looking glass and the data ' 3700–4900 BLUE ' may be read, reference being to the designed reflective band width in ångström. This brief resumé of losses at the mirrors where maximum reflection is the aim, may be logically followed by similar attention to the lenses in the optical train where reflections reverse their role and become a loss.

The fraction R of the incident light that is reflected at the interface between two transparent media is :

$$R = \{(n' - n)/(n' + n)\}^2$$

where n and n' are the refractive indices of the first and second medium respectively. Thus, at the first surface of any lens in air, either singlet or compound, the loss by reflection is $\{(n-1)/(n+1)\}^2$ where n is the refractive index of the singlet (or of the first element of a compound lens). Similarly the loss at the final surface of either lens is $\{(1-n)/(1+n)\}^2$ where n is the refractive index of the singlet (or of the last element of a compound lens). The equation is also used to determine the losses in a compound lens at the interfaces of the elements in contact. On this basis, uncontrolled reflection losses at the first surface alone, range from $0 \cdot 041$ ($4 \cdot 1$ per cent) for the lightest crown glass ($n = 1 \cdot 51$) to $0 \cdot 073$ ($7 \cdot 3$ per cent) for the heaviest flint glass ($n = 1 \cdot 74$) but, because of the variation of n with wavelength, losses are slightly higher in the blue and lower in the red.

Fortunately, these losses may be reduced to about $0 \cdot 013$ and $0 \cdot 019$ respectively by coating the glass surface with a single film of magnesium fluoride of optical thickness one quarter wavelength—physical thickness about 120 nm—a readily available process called blooming. The most effective reduction of reflection losses is attained with the more complex multilayer dielectric coatings (lower curves, fig. 4.19), where surface reflection is held to $< 0 \cdot 003$ ($0 \cdot 3$ per cent) with practically zero reflection in one or two narrow wavebands.

It remains to deal with absorption losses within a medium. The proportion of light incident at one plane within a medium which passes a second plane within the same medium is called the transmissivity of the medium. It is expressed as $T = I_d/I_o$ where I_o is the light intensity at the first plane and I_d is the reduced intensity after transmission through thickness d of the medium. Here, $I_d = I_o e^{-kd}$ where d is the path length and k is the absorption coefficient, a value to be found in the glass makers catalogued data. The reciprocal of the transmissivity of a medium is called opacity, O, of which the logarithm to the base ten gives the optical density, D. This is a useful way of defining optical density, for in this form it is proportional to glass thickness and when light is transmitted through a number of elements, the addition of the separate densities gives the combined density. Thus, an element which (excluding reflection losses) transmits 0·95 of the incident light, has an opacity of $1/0·95 = 1·053$ and an optical density of $\log 1·053 = 0·0223$.

Further losses are suffered in ancillary equipment (see Chapter 7) but really need no further explanation as the methods given in this chapter apply to any optical train. Losses which arise from other causes, for example at the photographic plate or spectrograph slit, will be pointed out as they occur in the text. There are also many crystalline dioptric materials, which have properties very different from those of glass and are essential for work on either side of the visible spectrum. They will be reviewed in Chapter 11.

CHAPTER 5

telescope engineering

THE large modern telescope is as much a product of engineering as of optical science for while the development of telescope optics will result in construction of at least six instruments of 3 to 4 m aperture during this decade, it could not have been so without similar advances in engineering. As primary mirror apertures increase, mechanical and structural difficulties increase disproportionately because the areas of structural members tend to increase as the square of a linear dimension and the resulting extra flexibility is aggravated by structure weight which tends to increase as the cube of a linear dimension. Mirror profiles, so carefully computed and produced, are heavily dependent upon the engineering design of mirror cells and mountings to ensure that they will retain their profile accuracy in any attitude of the telescope. Increased structural stability is required in order to derive benefit from the improved resolving power obtained from larger apertures and an inadequate structure would waste this very costly gain. Inspection of a modern telescope shows that the optical glassware represents a very small proportion of the bulk and weight of the complete instrument.

5.1. *Basic parameters*

The parameters to be fixed first are aperture diameter and focal ratio, and these values set the pattern for design and construction during the years which will elapse before completion. As late as 1970, of the world's 220 observatories, only 15 had telescopes of 1·2 to 1·5 m aperture and only 4 observatories exceeded 2·5 m, plus of course, the 200 inch Hale reflector of Palomar Observatory. Up to this time, telescopes (with the exception of the Hale) were traditionally of about $f/5$ primary focal ratio which required a telescope tube length a little in excess of 8 m for a 1·5 m aperture instrument, and presented few engineering problems. But the latest generation of instruments, up to 4 m aperture, would require tubes more than 5 m in width and about 21 m in length for a similar focal ratio, and engineering problems would then become formidable. So although $f/5$ was considered to be the optimum focal ratio for earlier instruments of typical large aperture which produced a bright image of satisfactory size, the new large telescopes all tend to primary focal ratios of $f/3$ or less, cutting the tube length for a 4 m instrument to little more than 13 m. The shorter the tube, the lighter it is for a given stiffness, resulting in reduced loads on the bearings, lower power for the driving mechanism and less weight at the main frame ; the gains are cumulative. But by far the greatest advantage of a shorter tube arises from the smaller observatory building and dome required, for the capital investment here is very high and is related to size.

The focal length of a 4 m, $f/3$ instrument is of course 12 m which, being greater than that of say, a 1·5 m, $f/5$ telescope at 7·5 m, focuses a larger and brighter image of an object of finite size, than could be obtained by the earlier class of larger focal ratio. It may seem paradoxical, but a 35 mm pocket camera with a focal ratio of $f/2·8$ will, regardless of aperture, focus a brighter image of an extended object (let us say the Moon) than will the 200 inch Palomar giant of $f/3·3$. The reason is found in the size of the images which are proportional to the focal lengths of the lenses or mirrors producing them. These focal lengths are about 40 mm for the camera and 660 inches (nearly 17 000 mm) for the telescope.

These basic parameters are sometimes conditioned by circumstances. Thus, the Isaac Newton telescope of the Royal Greenwich Observatory is of 98 inch aperture because in 1949 a Pyrex blank of this diameter was presented to the British Admiralty by the MacGregor Trust, U.S.A.

The 120 inch reflector of the Lick Observatory is so because the test flat originally made for the 200 inch Hale telescope was of that diameter. Having served its purpose, it became the blank for the Lick primary mirror, which while being a modern telescope, has a focal ratio of $f/5$ because the blank was too thin to grind into its thickness the depth of concavity (sagitta) needed for a focal length of 360 inches and hence an aperture ratio of $f/3$.

The new Kitt Peak telescope, intended as a 150 inch instrument, is in fact of 158 inch aperture because the mirror blank turned out to be usable at that diameter. The original focal length however was retained to keep the tube length short, so the intended primary focal ratio of $f/2·8$ was revised to the very low value of $f/2·6$ for the constructed telescope.

5.2. *Producing a primary mirror*

Mirror materials have improved immensely since speculum-metal was displaced by glass, which in turn has been displaced by a variety of improved dielectric glass-like materials from Pyrex to fused quartz, now supplemented by the most modern glass/ceramic compounds, best known by trade names such as Cer-Vit and Zerodur. Minimum thermal expansivity is the primary consideration and this has improved steadily from 8×10^{-6} (glass), 3×10^{-6} (Pyrex), $0 \cdot 5 \times 10^{-6}$ (quartz), $< 0 \cdot 1 \times 10^{-6}$ (Cer-Vit), all per kelvin. Additionally the glass/ceramics have the advantage of a crystal size in the scale of light wavelengths. The superiority of the glass/ceramic mirror is not unanimously acknowledged, but its relatively low cost makes it an attractive choice. Serious difficulties attend the casting of the great mirrors. It is difficult to get sufficient material in a single melt and the cooling process has to be retarded to take place over many months to minimize internal stresses. Quartz (which is still considered by many experts to be superior to the glass/ceramics), cannot be cast into a large blank from a single melt, yet many of the present large instruments are being equipped with quartz mirrors.

Figure 5.1 shows the solution to the problem of obtaining large diameter blanks. It illustrates the primary mirror of the European Southern Observatory 3·6 m telescope, mounted in its cell at an advance stage of polishing, in the optical test shop of Recherches et Etudes

Fig. 5.1. The primary mirror of the European Southern Observatory (ESO) 3·6 m telescope in the optical test shop. *Recherches d'Optique et de Sciences Connexes, Ballainvilliers.*

d'Optique et de Sciences Connexes, France. It is clearly fabricated from seven hexagonal and six triangular pieces of quartz, and these are fused into a single great disc at a temperature of 2500°C. The small circular markings (apparently upon the face) are, in fact, support pads behind the mirror, seen through the uncoated face. The large, pale ring at the top of the mirror is an imperfection consisting of numerous minute bubbles, deep within one hexagon and so out of harm's way.

Once the mirror blank is delivered to the glass-working shop and grinding is started, its progress (except perhaps for the final figuring and polishing) is governed entirely by highly specialized engineering techniques. Figures 5.2 and 5.3 show stages during the manufacture of the primary mirror for the 158 inch telescope of the Kitt Peak National Observatory, Arizona, U.S.A. At fig. 5.2 the mirror has been edge-ground and the facing surface is being aspherically ground from its previous basic spherical form to meet the requirements of the Ritchey-Chrétien solution. The swirls of abrasive material on the mirror face trace out the loci of the square grinding pads relative to the mirror which result from rotary motion of the later and orbital motion of the grinding-

Fig. 5.2.   Grinding the aspheric surface of the primary mirror for the Kitt Peak National Observatory (KPNO) 150 inch telescope. *KPNO, Arizona.*

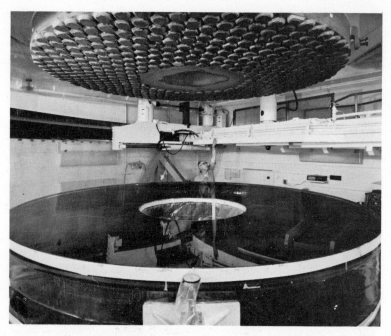

Fig. 5.3. Polishing the primary mirror for the Kitt Peak National Observatory (KPNO) 158 inch telescope. *KPNO, Arizona.*

pad spider. Note the varying radial positions of the pads and the running adjustments to the pad loads which are being carried out by technicians. Figure 5.3 shows the mirror receiving the early stages of polishing to the aspheric form on the same machine. The massive, multi-surfaced tool suspended over the mirror is a pitch lap such as is commonly used to perform this crucial operation. The reflections you can see are due to the quality of the finish alone, for there is no applied reflecting coating at this stage. Note the central Cassegrain hole.

5.3. *Telescope mountings and the coudé ray path*

With very few but notable exceptions, all large telescopes are equatorially mounted. This means that one of the two axes about which the telescope is driven, is set parallel to the axis of the Earth's rotation and is termed the *polar axis*. The reason for this will be dealt with in Chapter 6. The second axis is called the *declination axis* and is set at exactly 90° to the first.

Figure 5.4 shows an offset equatorial mounting applied to the 1·2 m reflector of the Dominion Astrophysical Observatory, Victoria, B.C.

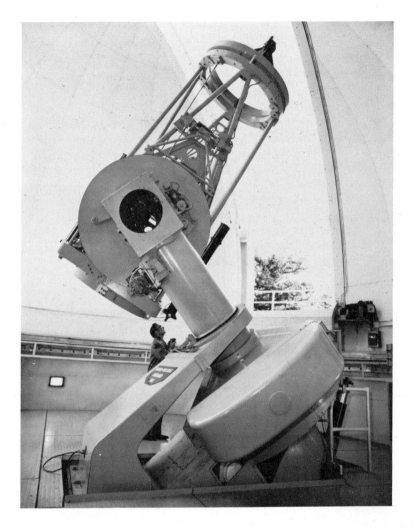

Fig. 5.4. The 1·2 m reflecting telescope of the Dominion Astrophysical Observatory (DAO), on an offset equatorial mounting. *DAO, Victoria, B.C.*

The offset form, in which the telescope tube and polar axes are not coplanar, is advantageous for telescopes of fairly small aperture because if the size of the instrument does not permit a telescope-riding observer, free access to the Cassegrain focus direct from the elevating observing floor (like a lift) is essential ; the photograph shows this convenience. The polar axis is through the tubular member in the centre of the picture.

Because the telescope is offset to this axis, its mass has to be balanced by the counterweight in the foreground and this *doubled* equipment weight, coupled with bending moments arising from asymmetry, disqualify this kind of mounting from service with the larger and heavier instruments. The telescope shown was used for developing the highly efficient coudé system mentioned in Chapter 4.

A coudé spectrograph ray path is often longer than its associated telescope, which precludes the spectrograph from being mounted upon the telescope. So, to serve the great spectrograph, light gathered by the telescope in every possible attitude must be directed to focus at a fixed position in the coudé slit room, a chamber which is usually below the observing floor. Figure 5.5 shows how this is arranged for the offset

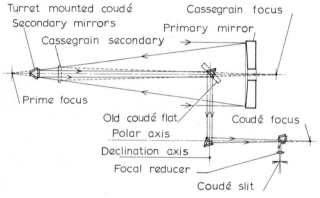

Fig. 5.5. Light path to the coudé spectrograph slit for the 1·2 m reflecting telescope of the Dominion Astrophysical Observatory (DAO). The three turrets of flat mirrors in the coudé ray path are driven simultaneously with the turret of coudé secondary mirrors, to bring into optical alignment complete sets of coudé mirrors which are highly reflective in narrow spectral bandwidths. *Adapted by permission of the DAO, Victoria, B.C.*

mounting of the telescope in fig. 5.4. The primary mirror, coudé secondary and first coudé flat (the latter located at the intersection of telescope tube and declination axes) all keep station with the telescope and so direct the beam out of the tube through the declination axis, to fall upon the second coudé flat at the intersection of declination and polar axes. The second flat rotates with the telescope about the polar axis, but not about the declination axis. Thus the finally reflected beam passes through the polar axis shaft to the fixed coudé focus. Figure 5.5 also shows the approximate sizes of the Cassegrain secondary and the earlier first coudé flat (both dotted).

The new coudé mirrors are multilayer coated (see Chapter 3) and because they are highly reflective in restricted bandwidths only, three small mirrors, each reflecting in different spectral regions, are mounted upon power-driven turrets at each of the three positions. All three turrets rotate and locate simultaneously, under automatic control. Two of them are seen at fig. 5.4, the secondary turret protruding from the upper end of the telescope and the second-flat turret through the large hole on the declination axis, the cover of which has been removed for the purpose. The big advantages of this development are minimal reflection losses and the small size and mass of the turrets, which results in only a very small area of the primary mirror being obscured from starlight, small structural deflection and a lighter counterweight.

But because of the small angle at which rays converge to the coudé focus from such a tiny secondary mirror, (equivalent focal ratio is $f/145$) a turret-mounted focal reducer serving two purposes is placed 2 metres in front of the focal plane as shown at fig. 5.5. One purpose is to fold the beam through 90° to make it conveniently horizontal for the coudé spectrograph, the other is to reduce the equivalent focal ratio from $f/145$

Fig. 5.6. Slit room beam-folding turret and focal reducers of the 1·2 m reflecting telescope of the Dominion Astrophysical Observatory (DAO). *DAO, Victoria, B.C.*

to $f/30$, which is the normal modern value for this focus. A photograph of this compact mechanism is shown at fig. 5.6. The three rectangular turret-mounted beam-folding mirrors are driven simultaneously with the turrets in the telescope and provision is made for five ratio-changing lenses. Reference to these mirrors is made on page 72, Chapter 4.

For telescopes of larger aperture than the DAO 1·2 m instrument, the offset mounting is no longer adequate and such instruments are mounted symmetrically according to one of the four forms, or their derivatives shown simplified at fig. 5.7. In each case PP_1 is the polar axis and for nothern hemisphere instruments, P points to the north celestial pole. DD_1 is the declination axis, D to the east and D_1 to the west. The telescopes, shown as closed tubes for convenience, are all illustrated in the normal stowed attitude, that is pointing to the zenith (exactly overhead) because in this position, asymmetrical stresses in the telescope tube and the two main mirrors are absent.

The fork mounting, fig. 5.7 (a) gives excellent sky access but suffers cantilever deflection at the fork blades and high bearing loads, particularly at the north bearing.

The yoke mounting, fig. 5.7 (b), has no cantilever deflection problems and benefits from equally distributed bearing loads. The disadvantage is that the north bearing obstructs telescope access to the north celestial pole (the extension of the terrestrial pole into space).

The horseshoe mounting, fig. 5.7 (c), has all the advantages of the yoke type and solves the problem of polar access by including a north bearing of sufficient size to receive a cut-out into which the telescope may be driven to alignment with the celestial pole.

The polar disc mounting, fig. 5.7 (d), is immensely rigid for a given weight and size. The conventional polar shaft is replaced by a thick, hollow rotatable disc, upon the north face of which the fork blades carrying the declination bearings are fixed. Deflections are minimal and sky access is complete at north temperate latitudes, except for a small part of the southern horizon.

A further type of mounting is the altazimuth in which one axis is permanently vertical and the other is at 90° to it and therefore permanently horizontal, regardless of the latitude of the site. The great Russian 6 m telescope, which will be the world's largest when it eventually goes into service, is so mounted. There are many advantages, mainly connected with symmetrical geometry and loading, and some disadvantages such as a rotating field and a drive system in which the two axes have a very complex angular velocity relationship in star tracking. It must be said that the increasing application of computer control to telescope drives (Chapter 6) eases the problem and the altazimuth may well find more favour in the future than it has had in the past.

Every large modern telescope has the coudé focus facility that has already been described for the 1·2 m instrument of the DAO, but the ray path shown in fig. 5.5 clearly cannot be adopted with the symmetrical mountings illustrated on this page. Nevertheless, by appropriate

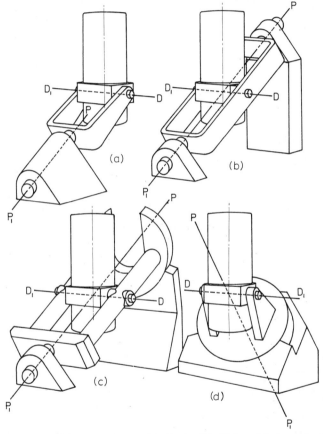

Fig. 5.7. Equatorial mountings. (a) Fork, (b) Yoke, (c) A variant of the horseshoe, (d) Polar disc.

location of a system of flat mirrors, the light rays are directed past all obstructions for all attitudes of the telescope, to the fixed position of the coudé focus. Three such ray paths associated with specific telescopes are shown in Chapters 7 and 9. They are the 200 inch Hale reflector of Palomar (horseshoe), the 98 inch Isaac Newton reflector of Royal Greenwich Observatory (polar disc) and the 2·2 m reflector of the Max

Planck Institut für Astronomie (fork). All have three-, four- or five-mirror coudé systems, some requiring one or more flat mirrors to be driven at half the telescope speed. In the majority of cases the coudé beam emerges from the telescope through the polar shaft, but in some cases, for example the 2·2 m of MPIA and the 60 inch infrared telescope of Tenerife (also described in Chapter 9) an alternative exit is used.

5.4. *Flexural errors*

Defects in images arising from an imperfect profile, or imperfect positioning, of the primary mirror are irreversible and so great attention is given to keeping up accuracy of the original optical design parameters for any service condition encountered. This really means for any attitude of the telescope, and throughout the temperature range encountered at the location of the observatory. One of the chief difficulties arises from the flexibility and weight of the mirror. If stood on edge and unsupported, the circular disc sags to an elliptical shape ; if it is laid horizontally and supported round the periphery it sags at the centre, while if it is supported with uniform upward pressure (thrust per unit area) over its entire rear surface it sags *at the edge*, because the material is thicker and thus of greater mass per unit area at the edge than at the centre. Compensation at these extremes of attitude alone is no solution, because the compensating force vectors will have to change sinusoidally with the zenith angle of the telescope. The suspension of the mirror in its cell to satisfy this condition is generally managed by mechanical linkage or by hydrostatic devices.

5.5. *Mirror cells*

Figure 5.8 is a diagram showing the principles of several mechanical mirror-support systems which vary only in detail and in sophistication. The mirror and its cell assembly is shown in the zenith position.

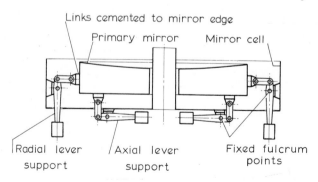

Fig. 5.8. Lever suspension primary mirror cell.

Cemented to the edge of the mirror is an array of metal lugs to each of which is pivoted a link which connects it to one end of its associated radial support lever. This lever has a fulcrum fixed relative to the cell. It is pivoted tangentially to the mirror, and carries at its free end a pre-calculated weight. Behind the mirror is an array of similar lever assemblies which provide axial support, but here it is not essential to cement the lugs to the mirror as they are permanently pressed into contact with it by the lever weights. Although only two of each kind of compensator are shown, forty or more may be used for radial support, while many more axial units are disposed upon several concentric pitch circles (fig. 5.15) to distribute their support over the complete area of the mirror.

In the zenith position shown, there is no natural tendency for the mirror to move radially, and hence no restoring forces from the radial supports, because the centre of mass of each lever is vertically below its fulcrum. But because the axial support levers are horizontal and the

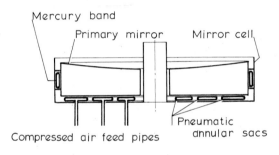

Fig. 5.9. Fluid suspension primary mirror cell.

turning moment about each fulcrum thus has its greatest value, the upward thrust at each mirror lug is also greatest and is adjusted so as to just support the weight of the assigned area of mirror that is above it. Those units in the outer row, where the mirror is thickest, are accordingly arranged to exert a greater upward force than those units which are on smaller pitch circles where the mirror is thinner. Now imagine that the cell is rotated about its diameter by 90°, so that its axis is horizontal. The axial supports exert no load upon the mirror because the centres of mass of all the levers and their fulcra are in the same vertical plane. The radial supports are now effective. All those below the horizontal centre line of the cell exert an inward radial force upon the edge of the mirror which, for a given lever-arm ratio, reduces progressively from its greatest value at the bottom of the mirror to zero at the horizontal. Those above the centre line exert an outward radial force at the mirror edge which increases progressively to its greatest value at the top.

We have examined the compensating forces generated at extremes of zenith angles and it can be proved that these lever systems can cope with the sinusoidal variation of the force vectors with changing zenith angle. This system is very effective and widely used, but it is not perfect. Bearing and pivot friction slightly degrade the result, and support at definite fixed points is not ideal. Figure 5.9 is a schematic diagram showing an improved design based on hydrostatic principles.

Radial support to the mirror is provided by a mercury-filled, flexible, endless tube (rather like a radially flattened road-wheel inner tube) confined between the wall of the cell and the edge of the mirror. The annular thickness of the mercury band, as it is called, is only a few millimetres, and its width is governed by the weight and diameter of the mirror, as will be shown presently. In the zenith attitude the mirror is subjected to an inward radial force, equally distributed around its circumference, but increasing linearly over the width of the mercury band due to the increasing depth, or pressure head, of mercury within. Thus there is no tendency to move the mirror radially.

Behind the mirror, and separating it from the bottom of the cell, are several (three are shown) flexible concentric, annular sacs (like axially flattened road wheel inner tubes), each a few millimetres thick and each of radial width dependent upon the mean slope of the annulus of the mirror surface that is above it. Each sac is inflated with air at a controlled independent pressure, sufficient to support the weight of mirror material above it. The pressure control device for each sac consists of an open topped cylinder mounted on the cell with its axis parallel to that of the telescope tube. At zenith, the cylinder axis is thus vertical. Within the cylinder a free piston (air-lubricated for frictionless movement) floats upon a compressed-air supply fed through a restricted orifice in the closed bottom end of the cylinder. Half way up, a vent hole in the cylinder wall communicates with the atmosphere, with the result that while the piston is held buoyant, partly exposing the vent hole, the air pressure beneath it exactly equals the weight of the piston divided by the cross-sectional area of the cylinder, regardless of supply pressure, so cylinders of the same diameter may be used for all sacs, the required pressure differences being obtained from pistons of different weight.

Again, imagine the cell to be rotated through 90° to the horizon. The hydrostatic pressure, p, in the mercury band at the bottom of a mirror will be $p = D \times 13\,600$ pascal (N m^{-2}), where D is the aperture in metres and 13 600 kg m^{-3} is the density of mercury, giving p about 540 kPa for a

4 m aperture mirror. This value decreases linearly to zero at the top of the band as one goes upwards. In effect, the mirror is *floating in mercury* although separated from it by the flat neoprene tube. From this condition the width of the band may be found, for a floating body must displace its own weight of the supporting fluid. Thus, if a disc of mercury has mass and diameter equal to the same parameters for the mirror, the disc thickness is the width of the mercury band

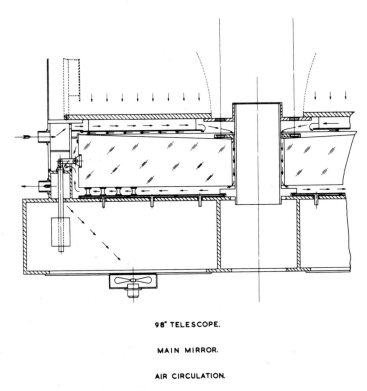

98" TELESCOPE.

MAIN MIRROR.

AIR CIRCULATION.

Fig. 5.10. Primary mirror mounting of the 98 inch Isaac Newton telescope of the Royal Greenwich Observatory, in its cell. *Sir Howard Grubb Parsons Co. Ltd.*

required to support the mirror. It is found to be about 0·2 of the mean thickness of a solid mirror, because that is roughtly the ratio of the density of glass to mercury. In this horizontal attitude of the telescope, the air pressure in the axial support sacs drops to atmospheric pressure because the pressure control cylinders are also horizontal and regardless of their weight, the pistons contained within them are blown past the vent holes in the cylinders, so communicating all the concentric support sacs with the atmosphere. As in the case of the mechanical linkage example, between these two extremes of zenith angle, the compensating forces adjust naturally and sinusoidally to changing zenith angle.

As well as load support, which is mainly concerned with holding the mirror to its designed profile, there is the further requirement of mirror position control and this is generally accomplished by slightly reducing the magnitudes of the supporting force vectors so that part of the mirror weight which remains unsupported, causes it to rest more firmly upon a pattern of radial and axial locators (sometimes called defining points) than upon the fully floating load supports. The locators vary in design from simple fixed-position jacking points on the smaller instruments to sophisticated mechanisms on the larger ones in which the mirror position is continuously monitored and the necessary accuracy is maintained by continuous, powered adjustment. Mirror location is invariably carried out at three axial location points behind the mirror and three or more radial locators around its edge.

Figure 5.10 shows a part section through the mirror cell of the 98 inch Isaac Newton reflector which employs mechanical leverage and pneumatic sacs for radial and axial support respectively. Note that the mirror is separated from the sacs by an array of 182 short, flexible-ended pillars (only four of which are shown), so that differential expansion between mirror and cell will not be transmitted as a lateral frictional drag between the two through the air sacs. The refrigerated air circulation across all the mirror surfaces is also of interest. The continuously monitored locators for the mirror are not shown in this view.

5.6. *Analysis of the structure*

Every permanently sited telescope ever built may be regarded as a unique instrument, even though the differences between individuals may be small. But current philosophy tends to a rationalized approach to the design of the 3 to 4 metre aperture class which is coming into service during the present decade. Because of this trend, and also because of the present day prominence of computer analysis techniques, the Canadian consultants, Dilworth, Secord, Meagher & Associates Ltd. (DSM), have devised a computer-based method of analysing telescope structures and the optical effects arising from deflections which, while not reduced to routine just yet, are tending to that end.

Figure 5.11 shows the DSM treatment applied to a telescope of fork-mounted design. For the purpose of computer analysis, the whole instrument is divided into five sections interfaced where structural

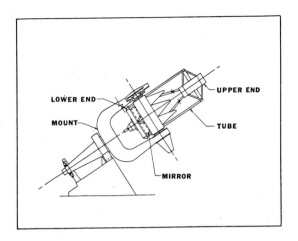

Fig. 5.11. Division of the telescope into units for deflection analysis by computer. *Dilworth, Secord, Meagher & Associates.*

interaction is simplest and hence where non-uniform deflections are minimal. They are (1) telescope tube, (2) mounting, (3) upper end, (4) lower end and (5) primary mirror.

The tube (1) has, until now, been considered as a genuine tube in the usual meaning of the word, but in the modern reflecting telescope it means that part of the instrument which is manoeuvrable on both axes and which houses the chief optical elements. It has a centre section through which passes the declination axis, and lower and upper sections which mostly take the form of the elegantly simple Serrurier truss. Any of the completed telescope photographs in this book, especially the model of the projected 3·5 m Italian instrument on page 169 illustrates the structural form far better than description. The outer ends of the struts of the upper Serrurier truss converge to support the upper ring, the lower (and much shorter) truss supporting the primary mirror cell in similar manner.

The mounting (2) may be any of those shown on page 83.

The upper end (3) is a cylindrical chamber called the *prime focus cage*, which is suspended on the optical axis by an array of thin, radial vanes called the spider, attached to the upper ring. The prime focus cage may contain a complex of observer accommodation, instrumentation, corrector lenses and cameras, focusing servo-motors and secondary mirrors for Cassegrain and coudé observing positions. The latter are motor-driven to the active position or to the ' stowed ' position according to the observing station in use at a given time. If a telescope is not large

enough to mount a prime focus cage of the size required for these different functions, several upper ends are held in readiness within the observatory dome, each designed for a smaller number of functions and each
quickly interchangeable by means of the specialized equipment installed.

The lower end (4) mainly consists of the primary mirror cell to which
are fitted all the devices necessary to maintain the mirror's optical performance against the adverse effects of gravity and of temperature
variation.   Attached to the back of the mirror cell is the Cassegrain
observing station equipped with observer's chair, camera equipment and
instrumentation, all of which is frequently mounted on a turntable.
It is here that the heaviest telescope-riding spectrograph, second in
power only to the fixed coudé instrument, is used, for on a large telescope, up to about 1000 kg of instrument mass can be accommodated.
There are power-driven adjustments to counterpoise the telescope
elsewhere, which maintains mechanical balance.

The primary mirror (5) requires very special attention to its suspension.

Two terms which are used frequently in the following text are
' rotation ' and ' translation ',   Rotation means angular displacement
of a component about an axis which is perpendicular to the axis of the
assembly to which it belongs.   For example, a mirror is *rotated* if it is
rocked, like a see-saw, about its own diameter.   Translation means
lateral displacement of a component from its correct position *in the
assembly to which it belongs*.   A mirror is translated for example, if it is
moved sideways, even with its cell, relative to the tube axis.

In analysing the tube, the upper end is substituted by a mathematical
model having the main spring-constants and weight distribution of the
real unit, and having its centre of mass coplanar with the attachment
points of the spider to the upper ring.   Simplification at the lower end,
in which the centre of mass of a rigid mirror and cell combination is considered coplanar with the apices of the struts that form the lower Serrurier truss, allows a computer readout of tube deflection for any
attitude of the telescope from the zenith to the horizon.   From these
results are obtained the gross rotations and translations of the upper and
lower ends, the behaviour of the upper and lower Serrurier trusses, the
upper end rings and the centre section.   Of particular interest in the
latter component is the deflection misalignment of the declination
trunnions, because maintaining exact squareness between declination
and polar axes is crucial.

In analysing the mounting, the computed tube load is applied to an
imaginary beam of equivalent spring-constant which connects the
declination bearings, and thus simulates the tube centre section.   The

effects of other external loads such as the Cassegrain cage, the coudé first flats, and the counterweights, are applied to the simulating beam which enables the computer to produce values for the declination bearing loads and deflections, the latter being critically related to the trunnion deflection.   Also computed are the gross movement of the tube in space, and the rotation and translation of the polar axis bearings.   This is very important, as we shall see later, to the safe operation of modern hydrostatic telescope bearings.

Analysis of the upper end considers the internal structure of the cage (or cages if there are several upper ends).   The computed results show additional deflections which generally lead to degraded optical collimation because of elastic deformation of the supporting structure. This question is very important, because experience shows that rotation of the cage components can be greater than the gross rotation of the cage itself.

Lower end analysis deals with deflections in the primary mirror cell and at the mirror support system components.   It also computes rotation and translation of the first coudé diagonal flat as well as the deflections caused by its support, where this takes the form of a tubular member passing through the central Cassegrain hole in the primary mirror.   Allowance is also made for Cassegrain instrumentation at this section.

The fifth analysis concerns the deformation of the primary mirror under the influence of its own weight.

5.7. *Tube deflection*

Figure 5.12 shows a link diagram for an ideal tube, complete with upper and lower ends.   The centre of mass of the upper end and the apices of the upper Serrurier truss are coplanar, the base of the upper and lower trusses and the declination axis are also coplanar, as are the centre of mass of the lower end and the apices of the lower truss.   With

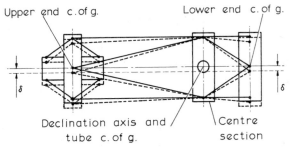

Fig. 5.12.   Deflections of an ideal telescope tube based on Serrurier trusses.

91

the tube pointing to the zenith there is no asymmetrical deflection of the tube and thus no rotation or translation of upper or lower ends. With the tube brought to the horizontal as shown, there is asymmetrical sag in the trusses (shown dotted) which causes a translation δ of the upper and lower ends but, let us say for the moment, no rotations. As the translation shown is the same at each end, there is no *relative* translation of the mirrors and so the optical performance remains unchanged.

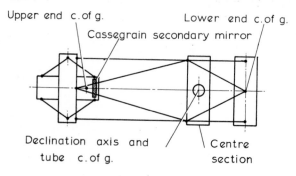

Fig. 5.13.   Practical telescope tube.

Figure 5.13 shows a practical link diagram for a large telescope with interchangeable upper ends where the secondary mirrors may be located perhaps 2 m (coudé) or 4 m (Cassegrain) inside the prime focus and the apices of the upper truss lie in a plane midway between the two centres of mass.   For practical reasons concerned with the attachment of the upper end, this plane is also arranged to coincide with the lower face of the upper end rings.   There is usually no great difficulty in arranging the ideal solution at the lower end (until the addition of the massive Cassegrain instrumentation upsets the load distribution) but an important variation arises at the centre section.   Both trusses are constructed from steel sections (usually tubes) having the same value of Young's modulus E, where

$$E = Wl/ax.$$

Here W is the tensile load on a specimen of the truss material of sectional area a, and x is the extension (or compression) of a length l of the specimen.   Now because the upper truss is much longer than the lower one, in order to obtain the same translation, δ, of the upper and lower ends (fig. 5.12), the linear strain x/l must be greater for the lower and shorter truss member than it is for the upper one.   If the lower truss is very short, which is usual, the required stress W/a rises to an impossibly high level and the truss is at risk.   The practical solution is to shift the attachment of the base of both trusses from the plane of the declination axis, to the upper surface of the hollow centre section, which shortens the upper truss and lengthens the lower one.

The result is seen in the photograph of the Isaac Newton telescope, fig. 9.2, where although the ideal link diagram has been modified as described, the tubes of the lower truss are much smaller in diameter than those of the upper truss. The resulting high linear stress and consequent strain produces the required translation of the lower end. In telescopes which have a high focal ratio, a lightweight upper end, or a very heavy lower end, even this departure from the ideal would overstress the lower Serrurier truss members. In these cases it is abandoned in favour of an array of equally spaced flexion members which lie parallel to the telescope tube axis. But for our purpose we will stay with the Serrurier truss.

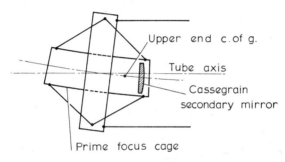

Fig. 5.14. Deflections of the upper end.

5.8. *Upper end deflection*

Figure 5.14 is a simplification, but it allows a closer examination of flexure in the upper end. Suspended as shown, the tubular prime focus cage assumes a trapezoidal form in its longitudinal section in the direction of the gravity field due to its own weight, because the material at the lowest part of the cage is in tension and therefore extended whilst at the opposite side of the cage conditions are reversed. More accurately the unit is slightly bowed, like the shape of a banana. The presence of the Cassegrain secondary mirror near the inboard end of the cage shifts the centre of mass of the upper end away from the ideal position and towards the primary mirror, which produces a couple tending to turn the cage about a horizontal axis that is usually within the axial length of the upper ring. The overall effect is to rotate the mirror, and to add a further translation to that which arises from sag in the upper truss. When the upper end is changed to one equipped for the coudé focus, the smaller secondary mirror is mounted nearer to the outboard end of the cage. Thus the centre of mass is shifted farther out, and a different deflection pattern results. The pattern will be different for each individual upper end.

It is always possible to bring the upper end centre of mass to the ideal plane by applying counterweights, but the price in total weight is too high. In a telescope of, say, 4 m aperture 1000 kg of counterweight may be needed at the upper end, requiring a further 6000 kg at the lower end to balance the whole tube, so adding 7000 kg to the declination bearing load and hence to the polar bearings, causing further flexures. The invariable procedure is to design for a specified rigidity of the tube as a whole.

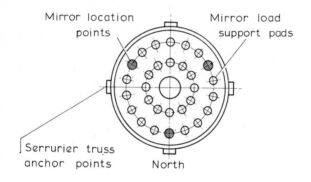

Fig. 5.15. Deflections of the mirror cell.

5.9. *Mirror cell deflection*

At the lower end, the primary mirror is not immune from rotation for the reason illustrated at fig. 5.15, which is an axial view of a schematic cell which has two concentric rings of axial support pads, shown as small circles. Three of these pads, equally spaced on the outer ring and shown hatched, are assigned as axial locators and thus carry more load than the rest. The four peripheral projections are the pick-up points for the apices of the lower Serrurier truss. All telescopes are collimated in the zenith position which means that the full weight of the mirror bears upon the axial pads with consequent elastic deformation of the cell bottom. The locators are then adjusted to align the mirror with the telescope tube and the remaining optical elements. The three locators and four pick-up points form an asymmetrical pattern about the east–west axis and driving the telescope down the meridian to the horizon produces mirror rotation proportional to the cosine of the zenith angle.

This is due to elastic recovery of the mirror cell, causing the north locator to move less than the other two because of its close proximity to the north pick-up point.*

5.10. *Results of mirror rotation and translation*

Having established that the mirrors rotate and undergo translation in service, and why they do so regardless of precautions taken, we may analyse the optical effects of the remaining unwanted mirror movements. These effects will mainly take the form of pointing error, that is deviation of the optical axis of the mirrors from the mechanical axis of the tube, and the introduction of coma into the centre of the field.

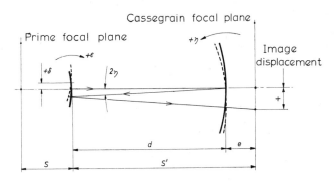

Fig. 5.16. Optical effects of rotation and translation of the mirrors due to structural deflection.

Figure 5.16 illustrates a primary and secondary mirror which have suffered rotations of η and ϵ respectively and a differential translation of δ. The collimated mirrors are shown in full line and the values assigned to the mirror displacements (shown dotted) are given positive signs. The focal length of the primary is f_1, the back focal length of the secondary is f_2 and the equivalent focal length of the combination is f. The linear displacement of the image at the focal plane is the sum of :

(1) η, arising from the assumption of a *flat* secondary $= 2\eta d + 2\eta S'$
(2) translation $2\eta d$ of the ray on the *curved* secondary $= 2\eta d(S'/f_2)$
(3) rotation ϵ of the secondary $= 2\epsilon S'$
(4) differential deflection δ which causes added ray translation at the secondary $= \delta S'/f_2$

---

* In fact, the telescope is never driven right down to the horizon because the primary mirror is at great risk of falling from the cell and secondly, the seeing is invariably very poor.

95

The image displacement is thus

$$2\eta(d+S') + 2\eta dS'/f_2 + 2\epsilon S' + \delta S'/f_2.$$

But

$$d + S' + dS'/f_2 = f,$$

so the expression may be written

$$2f\eta + 2S'\epsilon + S'\delta/f_2$$

Now the pointing error is

$$image\ displacement/f = 2\eta + (2S'\epsilon/f) + (S'\delta/f_2 f)\ \text{radian}$$

where η and ϵ are in radians and δ, f, f_2 and S' are in metres, or

$$2\eta + 2S'\epsilon/f + 206(S'\delta/f_2 f)\ \text{seconds of arc}$$

where η and ϵ are in seconds of arc and δ is in millimetres. Since $f = S'f_1/S$, the general expression for tube pointing accuracy in seconds of arc is

$$2\eta + 2S\epsilon/f_1 + 206(S\delta/f_1 f_2)$$

In fig. 5.16, if only the secondary mirror is considered to have moved, field centre coma in angular measurement is given by the expression

$$3\theta^2(m+1)(m-1)^2(f_2\epsilon/4f) + 3\theta^2(m-1)^2[(m+1) + e^2(m-1)]\delta 8 f_1$$

where θ is the semi-angle of the beam in radians (i.e., half the reciprocal of the Cassegrain focal ratio), $m = f/f_1 = $ magnification and e is the eccentricity of the hyperbolic secondary. The eccentricity of a conic-section curve is the ratio of the distance from any point on the curve to the focus, divided by the shortest distance from the same point to the directrix ; it is constant for a given curve. When, as in fig. 5.16, both mirrors are rotated, $\epsilon + \eta$ is written η, and $\delta + d\eta$ is written Δ.

5.11. *Polar and declination axis bearings*

The critical nature of the structural engineering evident from the foregoing, leaves no doubt about the requirement for similar care in the design of power transmission arrangements, especially for the highly loaded polar axis drive. Ball and roller bearings served astronomy well until 1948 when the 200 inch Hale telescope went into commission on hydrostatic polar bearings. Calculation showed, in design study, that the power required to drive the half million kilogramme movable mass about its polar axis on rolling bearings would measurably twist the telescope structure, and the alternative hydrostatic, or oil-pad bearing method, already established in the machine tool industry was selected. This technique was, and still is, outstandingly successful and all large telescopes built since then, including those being built now, employ oil-pad polar axis bearings either wholly or in part.

Hydrostatic principles use an external source of power to maintain a separating film of oil under pressure between two sliding surfaces. Figure 5.17 (*a*) shows this principle. A metal disc is ground accurately

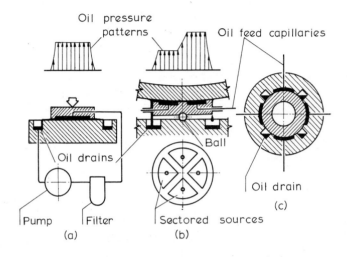

Fig. 5.17. Hydrostatic principles and application. (a) Basic principle, (b) Application to the north polar axis bearing, (c) Application to the south polar axis bearing. (northern hemisphere telescopes.)

flat on one side and into this surface a shallow, circular cavity called the source is formed, leaving an annular border of ground surface called the sill intact around it. The disc is placed source-side down upon a flat plate over which sliding is to take place, the source being supplied with a controlled flow of oil under pressure. When force-equilibrium is reached, continued oil flow into the source causes the disc to rise from the plate and an equalizing flow to leak from the resulting clearance between sill and surface to be collected, filtered and returned to the system for re-circulation. In this condition, the disc may be moved over the surface of the plate very smoothly and easily whatever the magnitude of any concentrically applied external load. Concentric loading is important because a single-source, freely mounted pad has no resistance to tilting and total loss of clearance at any point on the sill usually results in severe damage.

In telescope north bearing applications the hydrostatic principle is applied typically as in fig. 5.17 (*b*), to eliminate the risk of metallic contact in the bearing. The circular pad is mounted upon its back in a manner which allows limited freedom to tilt (bearing centrally upon a steel ball as shown is one method) and the upper face has four sources, each a 90° sector separated by an extension to the circumferential sill and each fed with oil under a separate flow control. The north polar axis assembly is supported radially upon at least two pads and if under drive conditions a pad tends to tilt relative to the polar shaft for any reason (which may include small flexures) a restoring force corrects matters immediately. A tilt as shown, gives differential sill clearance around the circumference and between the sources. Thus the leakage rate from each source is different, and because the flow rate into each source is strictly controlled, a pressure drop develops in the source which suffers the greatest leak rate and a compensating pressure rise develops in the source that is diametrically opposite, because here, the clearance is reduced. The difference in source pressures provides the restoring moment to equalize the clearance over the whole sill area. In practice, the normal clearance is about 0·1 mm and the response so rapid that the clearance differential rarely exceeds 0·04 mm.

The mean oil pressure of the sources times the effective area of the pad equals to the total load supported by the pad, which leaves the rate of oil flow as the only quantity which has to be controlled. Poiseuilles equation for the parabolic flow (non-turbulent, or streamline flow) of a viscous fluid in a circular-section pipeline is

$$Q = \Delta p \pi R^4 / 8 \eta l \tag{1}$$

where Q is rate of flow, η is the dynamic viscosity of the oil and Δp is the pressure drop in a pipe of radius R and of length l. The corresponding expression for the rate of flow through a narrow slit or its equivalent is

$$Q = \Delta p b h^3 / 12 \eta l \tag{2}$$

Equation 2 gives the requirements for the design of an oil pad where b is the mean sill length, h is the sill clearance and l is the dimension across the sill in the direction of the escaping oil flow.

The oil supply pressure at the pump is always considerably higher, perhaps by 100 per cent, than the design pressure in the source. Control is effected by feeding each of the four sources through a separate capillary tube from the common supply. When the leak rate from a source exceeds the flow rate through the capillary feeding it, the pressure in that source will fall and a pressure rise will develop in the source opposite, due to its reduced leak rate. Just as the *oil-pad* responds to design treatment as in eqn. 2, so will the *control capillary*, usually a fine-bore, thick-walled glass tube, respond as in eqn. 1.

In fig. 5.17 (c) the principles are shown applied to the south bearing in which all four sources are machined so as to be integral with the journal (that is, the hole) within which the shaft rotates. The smallest translation of this shaft within the journal results in a differential clearance, pressure, and hence restoring force similar to those described for the north bearing.

Hydrostatic bearings may also be used for the declination axis, but here the problems are more complicated because the bearing load vectors vary from mainly-radial to mainly-axial as the telescope is driven about its polar axis, where the vectors are constant. Drainage and collection of the oil for re-circulation also presents additional problems at the declination axis for the same reason.

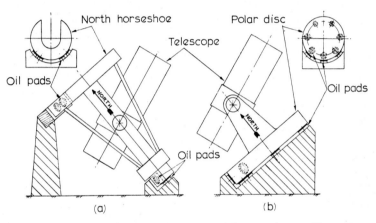

Fig. 5.18. Oil pad locations on two equatorial mountings. *Contemporary Physics.*

Figure 5.18 shows arrangements for hydrostatic bearings applied to horseshoe and polar disc equatorial mountings and fig. 5.19 is a photograph taken during the course of construction of the 98 inch Isaac Newton telescope in the workshop of its makers. The centre section of the polar disc is being lowered into place on the oil-pads, each of which is temporarily guarded by a protective cover. All three radial pads can be seen and six of the seven axial pads also. Further examples are to be seen on the north bearing of the 3·5 m Italian instrument on page 169 and the 158 inch of Kitt Peak on page 173.

5.12. *Improving the resonant frequency*

The very small torque and vibration damping obtained from hydrostatic bearings at the low drive speeds used for telescopes, tend to

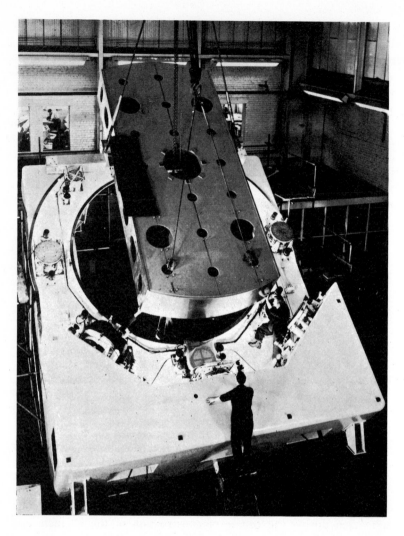

Fig. 5.19.   Lowering the polar disc centre section of the 98 inch RGO telescope
onto the oil pads.   *Sir Howard Grubb Parsons Co. Ltd.*

heighten the effect of driving gear vibration, observer movement and
wind action, all of which oppose the development of the most modern
photoelectric methods of guiding the telescope which even hold some
hope for following the high frequency excursion of the seeing image
(Chapter 4).   To help development, the entire telescope must have as
high a natural resonant frequency as possible, and for a given telescope,

B. Bertin (Observatoire de Meudon) suggests a revised sidereal drive system which raises this frequency by a factor of about two.

Traditionally, the drive is applied to the south end of the polar shaft, but Bertin moves the point of application to the horseshoe. Figure 5.20 shows block inertial diagrams representing the whole of the movable

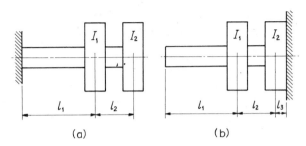

(a)   (b)

Fig. 5.20. Polar axis drive of a northern hemisphere telescope from (a) the south end and (b) the horseshoe. *Observatoire de Meudon.*

part of each of the telescopes considered. They are the 2 m and 3·6 m French instruments of INAG (Institut National d'Astronomie et de Géophysique). The structure is considered fixed at the plane of the drive (shown hatched); fig. 5.20 (a) shows the south end drive and fig. 5.20 (b) the revised horseshoe drive. The natural frequency of torsional resonance is given by

$$f = (1/2\pi)\sqrt{CJ/\Sigma Il}$$

where J is the polar moment of inertia of a constant-section shaft equivalent to the mounting, C is a coefficient representing its torsional elasticity, I_1 and I_2 are the moments of inertia of the telescope tube and of the horseshoe and l_1, l_2 and l_3 are the distances defined in the diagrams. Thus for fig. 20 (a),

$$f = (1/2\pi)\sqrt{CJ/[I_1l_1 + I_2(l_1 + l_2)]}$$

and for fig. 20 (b),

$$f = (1/2\pi)\sqrt{CJ/[I_1(l_2 + l_3) + I_2l_3]}$$

The horseshoe and the tube each represent roughly one third of the total rotating mass, so equation (b) has the advantage of raising the oscillation frequency firstly because $l_2 + l_3 < l_1$ but mainly because $l_3 \ll l_1 + l_2$. The advantage is shown to increase as l_2 decreases relative to l_1, that is, when the declination axis (and so the centre of mass of the tube) approaches the horseshoe.

101

Using formulae derived from the above expressions, values obtained for the two INAG telescopes are :
3·6 m, driven at the south end, 8·6 Hz ; at the horseshoe, 17·2 Hz.
2 m, driven at the south end, 13·9 Hz ; at the horseshoe, 26·3 Hz.

Because of the approximations used, these calculated frequencies are not absolute, in the sense that only the relationship between them is accurate, but the important outcome is the factor of about two by which the horseshoe drive improves on the south end drive.

drive and control

THE drive to a telescope keeps the ground-based instrument aligned exactly and continuously with a given reference point in space even though the Earth is rotating. Such a drive is most simply applied to the polar axis of the equatorially mounted telescope, because the polar axis of the instrument is set parallel to that of the Earth. If the instrument is driven at Earth's polar angular velocity, but in the opposite direction the motion necessary to maintain the required alignment is obtained.

6.1. *The equatorial mounting*

Figures 6.1 (*a*) and (*b*), each represent the Earth viewed from a distant point on the line of the north celestial pole ; thus the central point P is the north terrestrial pole in each case. In fig. 6.1(*a*) a *fixed* telescope mounted on longitude ' A ' is aligned to a star, and its progress is followed at two-hourly intervals during a period of 8 hours, when it will have swept a 120° sector of sky at the rate of about 15 minutes of arc per minute of time. At fig. 6.1 (*b*) the telescope is similarly aligned, but this time upon an equatorial mounting and the reader thus looks straight down the axis of the polar shaft. During the same 8 hour period, while the Earth has uniformly rotated 120° anti-clockwise, the telescope has been uniformly driven 120° clockwise about its polar axis, and the tube therefore remains aligned with the same point in distant space. The

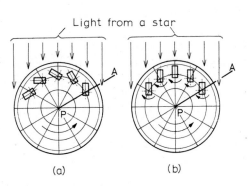

Fig. 6.1. Synchronism of the telescope and the Earth's rotation.

lateral displacement of the telescope across the face of the terrestrial disc during this period is so small relative to stellar distances that it has no effect upon image displacement.

6.2. *Timekeeping*

The crucial matter in maintaining collinearity between star and telescope tube is the timing, and this is more complicated than one may imagine as there are three time standards. They are civil, solar and sidereal time. The civil day of 24 equal hours is, in common experience a constant time interval equal to the *mean* interval between successive passages of the Sun across the observer's local meridian which is the projection onto the celestial sphere, of the line of terrestrial longitude upon which the observer is sited. If this line is the meridian of Greenwich, it gives a datum for universal timekeeping (G.M.T.) throughout the world.

The solar day is a variable time interval, its duration depending upon several factors, the two principal ones being conditioned by Kepler's second law of planetary motion and the inclination of the Earth's axis to the plane of the ecliptic, which is the plane containing the Sun and the Earth's orbit round it. Figure 1.3. showed that when the Earth, in elliptical orbit about the Sun, is closest to it (at perihelion) our daily orbital angular speed is greater than when we are farthest from it (at aphelion). Figure 6.2 shows the cyclic variations. The Earth is shown at eight positions on its orbit. A and B are separated by one day civil time interval ($1/365 \cdot 25$ year $= \alpha°$ orbit angle), equally divided by the spring equinox. E and F are similarly separated in time and distance and also equally divided by the autumn equinox. At the equinoctial

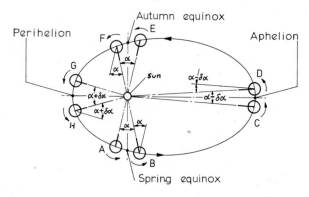

Fig. 6.2. Variation in the duration of the solar day due to the Earth's elliptical orbit.

104

points upon the annual Earth orbit, sunrise and sunset occur in the exact east and west respectively, and the periods of daylight and darkness are equal at 12 hours each all over the world except at the poles where the Sun skims the horizon for an extended twilight period before six months' daylight or darkness sets in, depending upon whether north or south pole is considered. The thick radial line marked upon each Earth diagram represents the datum meridian (let us say, the meridian of Greenwich) with which to measure the length of the solar day. In moving from A to B, Earth must rotate upon its axis by $360 + \alpha$ degrees to bring the meridian coplanar with the Sun once more and so to recover the noon condition as at A. Similar related motions prevail at the autumn equinox for a noon-to-noon interval between Earth positions E and F.

At aphelion, which corresponds approximately to the northern hemisphere summer solstice, the Earth is slower in orbit due to our increased distance from the Sun, but maintains its uniform angular velocity about its own axis. Hence if the datum meridian is in the noon position and therefore coplanar with the Sun when Earth is at C, it will be at noon again at D, but the Earth will only have rotated $360 + (\alpha - \delta\alpha)$ degrees, and the solar day will thus be shorter than at the equinoxes. Again, in the perihelion region corresponding approximately to the winter solstice, the datum meridian is at the noon longitude at orbital position G and the uniformly rotating Earth will present the plane of the datum to the Sun once more, and so to the noon position, in $360 + (\alpha + \delta\alpha)$ degrees of axial rotation at orbital position H. For these reasons alone, the length of the solar day varies in the ratio of $[360 + \alpha + \delta\alpha]/[360 + \alpha - \delta\alpha]$ or to the absolute extent of $\pm \delta\alpha$.

A further time variation arises because the plane of the celestial equator (the projection of the terrestrial equator into space) is inclined at 23° 27′ to the plane of the ecliptic. It is easier to understand this by imagining the observer stationed upon the Earth of a geocentric system. Figure 6.3 illustrates this and because at any instant the Earth–Sun relationship is accurate, the model is perfectly valid. If the variations of the Sun's apparent velocity demonstrated in fig. 6.2 are temporarily set aside, its angular velocity on the ecliptic may be considered constant. Therefore, starting from the spring equinox ϒ, the Sun's motion from ϒ to B on the ecliptic may be represented by the vectors ϒC on the equator and CB perpendicular to it. These are very important ordinates called the *Right Ascension* (R.A.) and the *Declination* (dec.) respectively.

Hence, for an angular excursion ϒB of the Sun on the ecliptic, its R.A., will have increased only by ϒB cos 23° 27′. But at the summer solstice

105

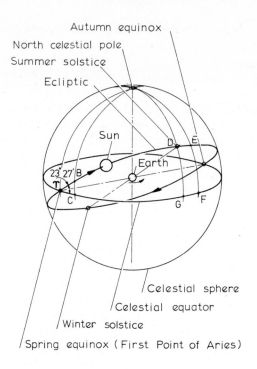

Fig. 6.3. Variation in the duration of the solar day due to the inclination of the equator to the ecliptic.

when the Sun reaches maximum north declination, its true angular motion DE on the ecliptic is momentarily parallel to the equator and its R.A. therefore increases at GF, at the same rate as its progress around the ecliptic. Similar variations occur at the autumn equinox and at the winter solstice when the Sun reaches its maximum south declination. The effects of figures 6.2 and 6.3 may be combined, for it happens that perihelion and aphelion of fig. 6.2 correspond fairly closely in time with the northern hemisphere winter and summer solstices respectively.

These variations in the length of the day, result in the Sun's transit across the celestial meridian almost 15 minutes late during February and a little more than 15 minutes early during November, by the standards of civil-time noon. The graph at fig. 6.4 shows the value of the solar noon variation related to the mean noon interval throughout the year. This variation from uniformity is called the *equation of time*, which is an archaic way of saying that which must be added in order to achieve equal times.

To the astronomer the most important scale is sidereal time. Figure

6.5 shows a small portion of the Earth's orbit around the Sun, exaggerated and simplified. As the duration of a year is 365·25 days, the mean daily orbital excursion of the Earth in orbit about the Sun is $360°/365·25 \approx 1°$. So if the Earth is considered to start from point A on its orbit, the heavy radial line on the Earth disc represents the noon meridian because the Sun lies on this plane. During one revolution, the Earth will have moved in its orbit to position B and the reference meridian will lie parallel to its starting position at A. The Earth has thus rotated exactly 360° relative to the distant stars and wherever the

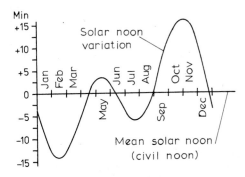

Fig. 6.4. Curve for the equation of time.

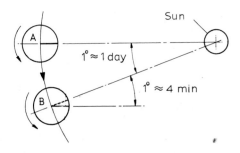

Fig. 6.5. Duration of the sidereal day.

Earth is on its orbit, the time required for this rotation is constant at 23 hours 56 minutes (civil time) and is called one sidereal day. For the convenience of astronomical co-ordinates, this period is divided into 24 sidereal hours and thence to sidereal minutes and seconds. But the Earth at B (fig. 6.5) still requires a further 1° of axial rotation to restore the reference meridian to the noon position, and this motion will take four minutes which, added to the sidereal day produces the civil day of 24 hours with which we are all familiar.

6.3. *Celestial co-ordinate points*

From here one may progress to a system (of which there are several) of locating celestial objects in the night sky in much the same way as the geographer or navigator locates objects on the Earth's surface in terms of latitude and longitude. On Earth the datum point is the intersection of the equator and the meridian of Greenwich, 0° latitude 0° longitude. On the celestial sphere the primary datum point is the First Point of Aries (♈), and this coincides with the spring equinoctial point where, (fig. 6.3) the ecliptic intersects the celestial equator. When first established, this point was in the constellation Aries but due to the precession of the equinoxes it now lies between Pisces and Aquarius, although it retains its original name. The equinoxes precess (that is, complete a revolution on the celestial equator) once in about 26 000 years, but such is the importance of ♈ that its location on the celestial equator is known to within 0·001 arc second at any time, and is published in such annual reference books as *The Astronomical Ephemeris*. From this reference point any star's position may be precisely identified by quoting two co-ordinate values. One is its declination in degrees, minutes and seconds of arc, either positive or negative depending upon whether the star is north or south of the celestial equator; the other is its Right Ascension in hours, minutes and seconds of sidereal time.

Declination is easy to set up, even manually, with an equatorial telescope, because the declination axis of the instrument is in the equatorial plane. (If the Earth's radius is disregarded by comparison with

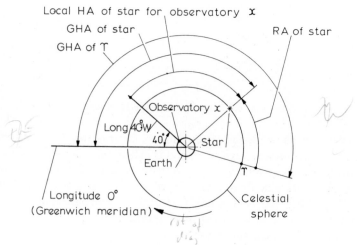

Fig. 6.6. Location of a star in Right Ascension.

108

astronomical distances, the telescope may be considered as being located at the centre of the Earth.) Thus if the tube is set at exactly 90° to the polar axis, the telescope will be precisely aligned with the celestial equator. From this setting it is equally simple to add or subtract the declination reference for the required star and to readjust the telescope to the required declination angle.

Finding the star in Right Ascension, is more complicated, and fig. 6.6 explains the procedure. It represents the celestial sphere observed from a distant point on the north celestial pole. The Earth is in the centre and a star having arbitrary R.A. is on the periphery. Two terrestrial lines of longitude are shown, one being the Greenwich meridian (long. 0°) and another arbitrarily chosen at long. 40°W upon which observatory X is imagined to be sited.

The local sidereal time on any terrestrial meridian is the *local hour angle* (H.A.) which separates it from ♈, and that which relates specifically to 0° long. is called *Greenwich Sidereal Time* (G.S.T.). The convenience of this time treatment is that the R.A. of a star is numerically the same as the local sidereal time at the instant of the star's transit across the local meridian. Although the Earth rotates west to east, in fig. 6.6 it is convenient to regard the central Earth as stationary, together with its two heavily marked lines of longitude (Greenwich and 40°W), and to restore the relative motion by rotating the rest of the diagram clockwise (east to west) around the fixed Earth. Thus the *Greenwich Hour Angle* (G.H.A.) for both ♈ and the observed star will increase as will the local H.A. of the star for observatory X. Right Ascension of the star, always reckoned eastward from the First Point of Aries, of course remains constant by definition.

Setting the telescope to intercept a star at a given moment in civil time at Greenwich, requires finding the G.H.A. of ♈ and hence G.S.T. corresponding to the chosen civil time, in such a comprehensive reference catalogue as already referred to. From the same source, the R.A. of the star is also obtained. Subtracting this value from the G.H.A. of ♈ provides the G.H.A. of the star. After one has set the telescope correctly for declination, it remains to set it for the G.H.A. of the star and wait for the chosen instant of civil time to arrive when the required star will be in the centre of the field. At this point the polar drive is engaged and the telescope will track the star until daylight or until it sets. In even relatively modern telescopes the R.A. and declination circles take the form of circular, vernier-divided scales which are fixed concentrically to their respective telescope axes and which can be read at the observing stations via simple optical systems. In very modern telescopes and those of the immediate future, the setting and reading functions will be automatic and the divided circles will then be relegated to monitoring.

To find the same star at observatory X on 40°W long., it is necessary to reduce the G.H.A. by the sidereal time equivalent of 40°, (2 hours 40 minutes). The same star will be centred in the field at the new site, presuming of course that it is within the manoeuvring capacity of the telescope at the time. This capacity depends upon the declination of the observed star and the latitude of the observatory, for whilst an imaginary telescope sited at the north terrestrial pole is geographically limited from 0° to + 90° in declination, it has unlimited H.A. capacity. Sited upon the terrestrial equator it is limited to ± 90° declination and ± 6 hours H.A.

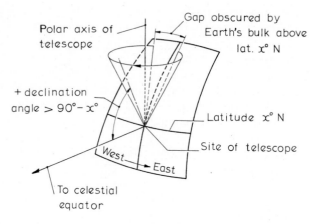

Fig. 6.7. Restriction of the circumpolar field by the terrestrial sphere. A small part of the northern hemisphere is shown. The discontinuity in the cone of revolution generated by the tube axis of a telescope sited on latitude $x°$N is caused by the obscuring effect of the terrestrial sphere north of the telescope, for any declination angle $< +90° - x°$.

Figure 6.7 shows a small section of the Earth's surface upon which an equatorial telescope is sited on latitude $x°$N, and set to a positive declination angle of $< 90° - x°$. As the Earth rotates west to east and the instrument is consequently rotated east to west, the axis of the tube generates a solid of revolution (a cone) which because of the restriction of the Earth's surface, has the discontinuity shown. If the telescope is set in declination to exactly $90° - x°$, the widest possible continuous cone of revolution is swept and the stars within it (which never set) are said to be circumpolar.

6.4. *Accuracy of the drives*

There are many disturbing effects with such elegantly simple drive arrangements. Chapter 4 noted a few, one of which is refraction by the Earth's atmosphere. A star at the zenith is seen at its true position because its rays enter the atmosphere perpendicular to the high altitude ' boundary ' of the air blanket and so (putting aside the effects of poor seeing), arrive at the observer undeviated by refraction. Some hours later, depending upon the latitude of the observer, the star will be seen apparently on the horizon, and just about to set. In fact, it will have set some minutes earlier, because light from the star is incident obliquely upon the air envelope below and beyond the observer's horizon and is refracted ' towards the normal ', entering the observer's eye from a point on the horizon where the star is about 0·5 degree below it. This effect, (clarified in fig. 6.8), and predictable image trans-

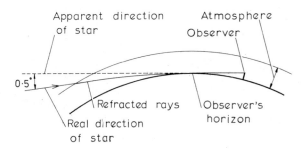

Fig. 6.8. Refraction through the atmosphere.

lations within the telescope due to structural deflections discussed in Chapter 5, are known as systematic variations and, in large telescopes of the present and future, cause few problems because the controller of the Right Ascension and declination drives is the computer—which may be programmed to compensate for such shifts.

There is at least one telescope however, the 120 inch of the Lick observatory, where the correction is arranged in another manner which is very difficult to fault. In this instrument the light-path deviation which increases with zenith angle is exactly compensated by the translation of the image on the Cassegrain focal plane due to deflections in the telescope structure. So setting this telescope up to R.A. and declination co-ordinates taken direct from the catalogue ensures that the required star will be in the centre of the field upon opening the mirror shutters. There is here no need to go through the usual procedure—to identify it in the wide-field ' finder ' (a small refracting telescope

111

mounted upon and parallel to the main telescope) and then to align the big instrument manually with the selected object before locking on and leaving the computer to take over.

To get an accurate 'feel' for the precision required from the R.A. and declination drives of the large instruments, it will be profitable to consider some numerical values. We will take as an example the 3·6 m telescope of the European Southern Observatory (ESO) which has headquarters in Hamburg, its Telescope Project Division at CERN, Geneva, and a selected site for its observatory at Cerro La Silla, 600 km north of Santiago de Chile. This instrument is fairly typical of the 3 to 4 metre telescopes coming into service soon at sites very carefully chosen, mainly in the southern hemisphere. After exhaustive trials carried out at this site since 1962 the seeing image diameter has been established as small as 1 arc second in normal conditions (which are exceptional by most standards) reducing to 0·1 arc second at intervals of rare seeing. Converting to linear measurement at the $f/8$ Cassegrain equivalent focal length of 28·8 m, the 'shimmer' disc diameter of a star image is normally 0·14 mm, 14 μm in exceptional seeing.

Due to the instrument alone, without reference to the seeing, a star image diameter is 0·5 arc second at the prime focus and 0·3 arc second at the Cassegrain station. In addition the specification requires 75 per cent of the collected light to fall inside a circle of 0·4 arc second diameter centred upon the star image at the Cassegrain focus and of 0·5 arc second diameter at the coudé slit. The finished mirror exceeds this requirement by focusing 94 per cent of the light inside the 0·5 arc second circle and 69 per cent inside a 0·24 arc second circle. Such optical precision must not be squandered by irregularity or inadequacy of the driving mechanism which, on this instrument, is required to keep the image of a star centred upon the photographic plate or spectrograph slit to within 0·1 arc second (14 μm at the Cassegrain focus) for several hours.

At an early stage in the drive design the decision has to be taken between installation of a worm and wheel transmission or a spur wheel drive. Each has its own special characteristics. In many large modern instruments we have seen a marked tendency towards rationalization, and one of the practices is to fit identical mechanisms to both the hour angle and the declination drives, although the duties are quite different. Excluding planetary observation, where perceptible motion of the nearer planets, even in declination during short periods, is apparent against the background of the stars, the declination axis drive is used, as we know, to set the telescope initially to the required angle of elevation, after which it will be activated only to make very small corrections to maintain collinearity between telescope and celestial object for the duration of the observation. But the H.A. drive is working both to locate the object and then to track it across the sky and it is thus active for the entire period of the observation.

Each axis can be driven at four separate angular velocities. They are :

(a) Slewing, a fast action, typically about 1 degree or more per second of time which is used for quick deployment of the telescope from the stowed position, or to re-direct the telescope for observation in a different part of the sky, or to driving the telescope to a position within the dome where facilities are installed for a quick change of top ends.

(b) Setting, an angular velocity of about 2 minutes of arc per second of time, used as a fine adjustment to bring the optical axis of the telescope to collinearity with the centre of the star field.

(c) Tracking, at sidereal hour angle (S.H.A.) velocity, 15 seconds of arc per second of time for the obvious purpose of keeping station with the observed object.

(d) Guiding ± 0 to 5 seconds of arc per second of time to adjust manually or automatically for the imponderables which randomly shift the image from the field centre, or any other position appointed for it.

The required accuracies range from about 5 per cent for functions (a) and (b) to 0·1 second of arc per second of time for function (c) and one per cent of even this tiny value for function (d).

Choice of drive

What can the engineer do to provide the astronomer's precisely timed drive? It is beyond human capacity to make, or even to measure, a gear train in which all the components are perfect. Variations range from eccentricity between the central shaft or hole and the teeth at the periphery of a wheel, worm or pinion, pitch (spacing) errors between adjacent teeth, cumulative pitch errors involving recurring groups of teeth, errors in tooth profile and so on.

There are sound technical reasons why a worm drive can be machined more accurately to pitch and tooth profile than the alternative drive employing spur-wheels and pinions. This is because the teeth of the worm wheel are machined using a cutter which has a profile replica of the worm which will eventually drive the worm wheel. In addition, a

I

valuable pitch-averaging function arises from the simultaneous engagement of as many teeth of the worm wheel as those of the worm in contact with it. This enhanced accuracy occurs with a normal industrial drive but the highest class telescope drive is further improved by the use of a duplex worm shown at fig. 6.9. The length of the worm follows the

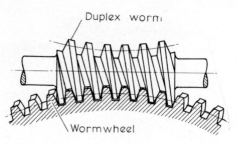

Fig. 6.9. Duplex worm drive. This differs from a normal industrial drive in which the worm is cylindrical and does not follow the circumference of the worm wheel.

circumference of the worm wheel, which results in a sinusoidal pitch variation in the worm to maintain constant relationship with the worm wheel, and a similarly changing pressure angle of the worm thread (or convoluted, single tooth), for the same reason. Add to this the very high velocity ratio, perhaps as high as 720 : 1 in a single reduction, and the worm drive has much to commend it.

There is of course, a debit side. A single-start worm drive with a reduction ratio that is in the region of our interest (' single-start ' refers to a single thread or tooth, helically machined on the worm) cannot possibly exceed 15 per cent in mechanical efficiency which means that over-powered drive motors are required, the wasted power being dissipated in very unwelcome local heat. A structural disadvantage lies in the fact that the maximum worm wheel diameter available from the largest machining facility in Europe is 5·2 m. Large enough, one may think, but not large enough for driving a 3 to 4 metre instrument at the horseshoe.

The alternative spur-wheel drive consists of a small pinion, with relatively few teeth, in mesh with a mating wheel bearing many times more teeth. Such gear wheels may be made up to 10 metres in diameter. There is an advantage attending the large driven wheel because for a given torque, tooth pressure is lower and this, coupled with a mechanical efficiency up to 95 to 97 per cent results in a cool, minimum-wear drive. But any errors of tooth pitch, tooth profile, or eccentricity are reproduced at the telescope on a cyclic basis. In a specific case, the French 3·6 m instrument, the pinion has 50 teeth and the wheel 2000 teeth, providing a velocity ratio of 2000/50 = 40 : 1 which, compared to the 720 : 1 of the worm drive described, requires more stages of gear reduction than does the worm drive, between the final pair of gears and the motors.

In the true spur wheel drive, the gear teeth are cut parallel to the shafts with which they are associated, an arrangement which tends to produce a highly efficient but slightly rough drive due to a very small jump ('cogging', to use the engineer's term), as each pair of teeth engages. The effect is most evident when the pinion has very few teeth, because the number of teeth in mesh with the large, driven wheel at a given instant is a factor in a parameter related to the number and size of the teeth and the pressure angle of the drive, called the contact ratio. It is an advantage to have this ratio as high as possible for a smooth drive without sacrificing too much of the geared reduction, but it is most important that the contact ratio should be in whole integers because a fractional ratio results in alternating engagement of one tooth above, then one tooth below the ratio with consequent fluctuations in tooth loading and hence deflection.

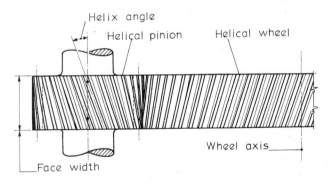

Fig. 6.10. Helical wheel and pinion drive, showing the pairs of teeth in mesh (marked with a spot) across the face width of the gears.

This undesirable effect is brought under control by cutting the teeth helically (fig. 6.10) thus avoiding a definite instant of engagement for the full face width of a pair of teeth. Helical engagement ensures that the line of contact between a pair of teeth progresses across the face width of the gear wheels during rotation. There are thus several pairs of teeth in mesh simultaneously across the face width of the gears on a line parallel to the shaft axes and the number of tooth pairs intersected

115

by this line are added to the contact ratio for a similar straight cut spur wheel drive, improving the value and producing a smoother drive. Correct selection of helix angle ensures that this complementary value not only raises the contact ratio, but also adjusts it to be a whole integer.

The two types of gear drive described above relate to the final geared pair in each case, the larger and thus slower wheels being attached to the polar shaft or to the declination trunnion of the telescope. There are obviously further reductions in the gear trains, the extent of which is shown in fig. 6.11 in the specific case of the H.A. and declination drives for the Anglo-Australian 3·9 m telescope installed at Siding Springs, N.S.W.

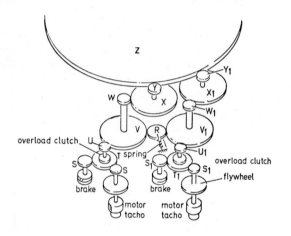

gear	number of teeth	DP or module	nominal PCD	gear ratio	
Z	600	6mm	141·73	} 24:1	
Y	25	6mm	5·906		
X	188	10	18·8	} 7·835:1	} 20,300:1
W	24	10	2·4		
V	240	12	20	} 12:1	
U	20	12	1·667		
T	180	16	11·25	} 9:1	
S	20	16	1·25		
R	34	12	2·83		

Fig. 6.11.   Right Ascension and declination power drives for the 3·9 m Anglo-Australian telescope.   *Ministry of Education, Canberra.*

116

Drives to both axes, shown in schematic form, are identical and there is duplication of every component of each drive, including the motors. This arrangement allows for the suppression of backlash in the system by coupling the duplicated drives together with an idler gear, that is, a gear which has no effect upon overall ratio. The idler, marked R (fig. 6.11) engages the duplicated wheels V and V_1 simultaneously and is spring biased in a direction which tends to shift it from its central position between these two wheels, so producing an equal and opposite torque in each gear train. Because these are independently driven at the power input (motor) end and constrained to common phase and synchronism at the driven end by the engagement of pinions Y and Y_1 with the great wheel Z, the torque from one motor supplemented at V by that resulting from the sprung idler R does the driving, whilst the torque from the second motor, reduced by similar torque of opposite sign at V_1, provides the restraining influence necessary for the elimination of backlash.

Columns 1, 2 and 5 of the table with fig. 6.11 are self explanatory. Column 4 lists the pitch circle diameter (PCD) for each gear in inches and column 3 lists identification of gear tooth size in two different standards of gearing. For gears Y and Z the module, 6 mm, times the number of teeth produces the pitch circle diameter in millimetre and for the remaining gears, the diametral pitch (DP), being an Imperial measurement standard, is the number of teeth per inch of PCD.

Suppression of backlash is to be arranged differently in the case of the French 3·6 m telescope of the Institut National d'Astronomie et de Géophysique. As with the AAT, there are to be duplicated driving trains, but in this case, no idler gear. Instead, each train will be driven by a bi-directional torque motor. During slewing, both motors drive in the same direction and the tooth loading is thereby halved, but during tracking one motor will drive while the other exerts a small restraining torque which will remove backlash from both trains.

In any gear train, each transmitting gear is certain to superimpose small cyclic velocity and displacement variations in driving the telescope through the full range of H.A. or declination capability. With multiple gears involved, while the maximum extent of these variations is known to the engineer in the design stage, the permutations are not. It is necessary to wait until the mechanism is built, to run it through the full range of both motions and then correct for the measured variations which occur. This is usually done either by shaping a cam designed to shift the cursor line of the measuring circle according to a precise compensating curve, and attaching the cam to the relevant telescope axis or, with the modern instrument, to prepare a computer tape with all the corrective data recorded upon it.

117

6.5. *Encoders, synchros and the computer*

We have examined the *basic* angular velocity of the H.A. drive, and how it is attained. We know that this is not good enough, due to the presence of both systematic and random displacement of the image from its true position. These irregularities may be rectified by manual observation and ' override ' at one end of the scale, and by pre-programmed, closed loop computer control at the other. But for the immediate purpose of discussing control of the telescope, we return to the 3·9 m AAT, typical of the large telescopes of this decade.

Figure 6.12 shows the schematic layout for the synchro and encoder drives which, like the power drives, are common to both major axes. In fig. 6.11 the gear wheel Z is the finally driven wheel attached to the telescope, and in fig. 6.12 it is the initial driving wheel for the encoders.

The manual input to a computer is usually in some form of code related to everyday mathematical functions and expressions, either numerical or algebraic, originating at a teletype keyboard, even though it may, in some cases, be stored on tape, card, or disc. Once fed into the computer, numerical values are converted to binary code, and the values will not be converted back to decimal until the computer presents the readout answers to the questions asked of it. Our treatment of this subject must necessarily be limited, but some understanding is needed in order to appreciate the function and principles of the shaft encoder.

The binary code is a digital system, that is a system in which values are varied in steps, and takes the form in which the arabic decimal equivalent is factorized in powers of 2, the indices decreasing as the factors are read from left to right. For example,

$$2^3 + 2^2 + 2^1 + 2^0 = 8 + 4 + 2 + 1 = 15.$$

The presence or absence of a power of 2 factor is denoted by the digits 1 or 0 respectively. Thus in the example given the binary code 1111 fully indicates the arabic 15 because all four power-of-2 factors are present. Similarly the binary 1011 would indicate the arabic 11 because the factor 2^2 is absent from the total. Binary digits (bits) can only be 1 or 0, so they can be fully represented by any form of on/off switching.

It is an asset for the computer input to be in binary, for then the outpost sending in the signals does so in computer-compatible form. An encoder is a rotary device, designed expressly for this function. Typically, it is an optical unit in which a rotatable glass disc is provided with as many concentric annular tracks as its bit (binary digit) capacity. It is also divided radially, producing a network of sections, some of

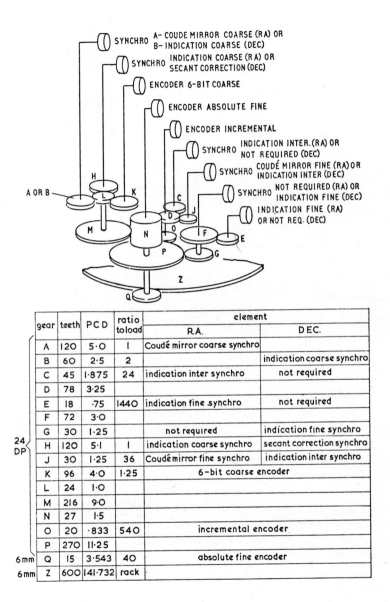

gear	teeth	PCD	ratio to load	element R.A.	element DEC.
A	120	5·0	1	Coudé mirror coarse synchro	
B	60	2·5	2		indication coarse synchro
C	45	1·875	24	indication inter synchro	not required
D	78	3·25			
E	18	·75	1440	indication fine synchro	not required
F	72	3·0			
G	30	1·25		not required	indication fine synchro
H	120	5·1	1	indication coarse synchro	secant correction synchro
J	30	1·25	36	Coudé mirror fine synchro	indication inter synchro
K	96	4·0	1·25	6-bit coarse encoder	
L	24	1·0			
M	216	9·0			
N	27	1·5			
O	20	·833	540	incremental encoder	
P	270	11·25			
Q	15	3·543	40	absolute fine encoder	
Z	600	141·732	rack		

24 DP (gears A–P); 6 mm (gears Q, Z)

Fig. 6.12. Right Ascension and declination encoder and synchro drives for the 3·9 m Anglo-Australian telescope. *Ministry of Education, Canberra.*

119

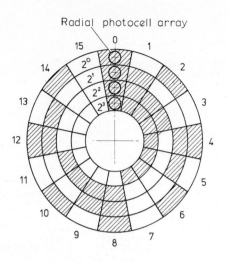

Fig. 6.13. Four-bit binary coded encoder disc.

which are opaque and some transparent according to a pattern appropriate to its duty. Figure 6.13 shows the pattern of the disc of a four bit encoder. The hatched areas are opaque, the white transparent. In front of the disc is an exciter lamp and collimating lens which directs a beam of light through the annuli, and behind it is a radial, narrow slot, exposing an array of four photo-electric cells, one in the radial position of each annulus. Rotation of the disc thus causes the four cells to be sequentially illuminated and obscured so providing the required on/off switching. The annuli from the outside to the centre represent increasing factors and are so marked, the position of the radial slot and the photocells reading 0000 (binary) = 0 (arabic) is shown in the all-opaque sector. The arabic value for each binary coded sector is marked around the edge of the disc for explanatory purposes only.

A four bit encoder is very coarsely divided but serves to demonstrate in a simple way that for a given attitude of the disc relative to the static radial slot, a unique switching pattern is obtained which the computer can ' read ' via a cable link. The absolute fine encoder in fig. 6.12 is a 15 bit unit, geared up 40 : 1 from the telescope axis, so producing $40 \ (2^{14} + 2^{13} + 2^{12} + \ldots . 2^{0}) = 1\ 310\ 680$ discrete signals per telescope revolution, that is, $360 \times 60 \times 60 = 1\ 296\ 000$ seconds of arc. The encoder is thus position sensitive to a little better than one second of arc of the telescope.

Just as encoders are digital devices for signalling the orientation of their switching discs, so the synchros, also shown in fig. 6.12 are analogue devices performing the same function in a stepless manner. So the output from them may be used to synchronously drive slave devices at cable-linked remote locations. These include indicating meters at the control desk and control of the drive to the third coudé flat mirror by the synchros associated with the polar axis drive.

Similar synchros at the declination axis compensate for changes in sensitivity of H.A. correction, proportional to the cosine of the declination angle. The AAT embodies an auto guider, controlling the servo system which applies the driving torque, and the auto guider sensitivity is greatest on the celestial equator, reducing to zero at the pole—for in this position unlimited H.A. drive does not deviate the telescope from pointing at the pole, so no error signal is produced by the auto-guider. The servo system will not function through this range of sensitivity because it is designed for a constant value and this is obtained by multiplying the H.A. error signals from the auto-guider by the secant of the declination angle. The declination axis synchros control this factor.

6.6. *Other computer functions*

Apart from the two major axis drives, there are many more functions under computer control in the observatory and fig. 6.14, which shows the control layout for the 3·6 m ESO telescope, is representative of present day outlook. Among these features are control of focus at the three observing stations (prime, Cassegrain and coudé). Focal variations are caused mainly by thermal expansion of the tube and differential expansion of the primary mirror which, because the edge is thicker than the centre, tends to shorten the focal length as the temperature rises.

There are several ways of monitoring these changes. Strain gauges secured to the Serrurier trusses will do so. A rod of material, of expansivity different from that of the tube material may be fixed to the lower end and free at the upper end where the differential expansion is measured continuously and signalled back to the computer. A taut wire of Invar, a metal alloy of very low expansivity may be stretched between upper and lower ends, in which case expansion of the tube results in three changes in the wire. These changes are : electrical resistance, tension and natural frequency of vibration, all of which may be used to provide signals. Resulting from this feedback of data, the computer activates the focusing motor appropriately, to restore image sharpness.

A very important control function is that of the fifth mirror (the third coudé flat) and the siderostat. The latter device is an altazimuth mounted flat mirror, installed outside the main observatory dome,

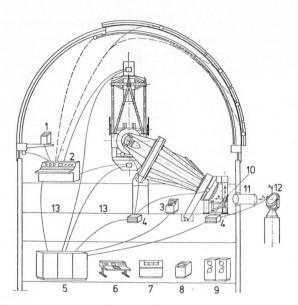

Fig. 6.14. The 3·6 m telescope of the European Southern Observatory installed in the dome, showing network of control devices. 1, Platform console. 2, Main console. 3, Coudé console. 4, Small computers. 5, Central computer. 6, Control panel. 7, Card reader. 8, Disc reader. 9, Magnetic tape reader. 10, Fifth mirror (Third coudé flat). 11, Auxiliary telescope. 12, Siderostat. 13, Coudé spectrographs. *ESO, Telescope Project Division, Geneva.*

(fig. 6.14) its purpose being to facilitate the simultaneous use of the main telescope and the great coudé spectrograph on different objects. If, for example, the main telescope is at work on a prime or Cassegrain focus study, the siderostat is driven in both elevation and azimuth so that the star under coudé examination is tracked across the sky. Its reflected light is directed through the tube of the fixed, horizontal, auxiliary telescope, which may be a relatively small refractor or a small offset reflector. The fifth mirror is then driven to a datum position where it directs the converging light from the auxiliary telescope to focus upon the coudé slit.

The only way to drive an altazimuth mounting with optical precision is under computer control, regardless of whether the mounted equipment is a telescope, siderostat or heliostat (which performs in similar manner relative to the Sun). Because the altazimuth mounting does not have the convenience of a direct polar axis drive, elevation and azimuth axes are driven simultaneously and at such related velocities that equatorial motion is imparted to the mounted equipment. Complete treatment of the altazimuth cannot be given here, but it is important to note that while this form has many excellent features from an engineering viewpoint, one disadvantage is that it has no access to an area of sky a few degrees in diameter, centred upon zenith. To track a star in this region requires an azimuth drive which reduces to infinitesimal angular velocity at the zenith point and this cannot be achieved, even with computer aid.

A further altazimuth application is the great dome drive in which the dome itself is driven in azimuth and the shutter and windshields in elevation. Figure 6.14 shows a four-piece shutter, the sectors of which are manipulated to provide maximum wind protection for the telescope. The zenith restriction does not apply to the dome because the shutter slot is usually about twice as wide as the mirror aperture and the drive requirement is far less precise. Further control duties, too numerous to list, remain for the computer and one very important function is day-time processing of data recorded during observing hours.

What do such sophisticated equipment and facilities offer to the observer? First, there is optimizing the performance of a very expensive installation which, in the 3·5 to 4 m aperture range, may have capital value upwards of M£5 sterling (1970 costs). Secondly there is the fast execution of complex control functions from such simple instructions as

(a) Go to next star.

(b) Correct for atmospheric refraction.

(c) Correct for driving gear errors.

(d) Drive dome as necessary.

(e) Drive coudé mirror 5.

In an open loop system these instructions, suitably coded, are typed on a teletype keyboard (very similar to a typewriter) and are received by the computer which then makes the necessary computations from stored data and sends appropriate commands to the object to be controlled. A closed loop system supplements the procedure by a feedback of information from the controlled device to the computer, indicating how accurately the command has been carried out and further refining instructions are given when required.

As an example of instruction (a), above, the computer draws upon stored data for R.A. and declination of the next star in a programmed sequence and reads the present position of the telescope from the position-encoders. Local sidereal time is monitored continuously from the observatory time standard, from which the exact position of the next star relative to the telescope tube axis is computed. Both major axis drives are activated by computer command into slewing motion under controlled acceleration. The value of the acceleration is fed back to the computer from a telescope-driven signal, this being very important as an excessive acceleration causes high gear tooth loading with the possibility of damage. At the conclusion of the slewing motion, the telescope is decelerated within a degree or two of the required star, and the final guide alignment is followed by normal tracking. Superimposed upon this sequence are the corrections computed from stored data, on systematic variations and further corrections computed from signals arising from such random variables as local meteorological data.

7.1. *Spectroscopy*

SPECTROSCOPIC equipment is named according to purpose. Thus, a spectro*scope* produces a spectrum observable through an eyepiece, a spectro*meter* enables the positions of lines in a spectrum to be measured, and a spectro*graph* is a specialized camera for producing a spectro*gram*, that is, a photograph of the spectrum. Light entering the instrument is dispersed by transmission—through either a prism or a diffraction grating, or by reflection from a diffraction grating.

The principles of the modern prism spectrograph differ but little from those of the earlier instruments ; only the details have changed. It is used mainly at the Cassegrain position. The star image is focused upon the spectroscope slit by the main telescope. The pencil of light passing through the slit thus diverges with a semi-angle equal to half the reciprocal of the Cassegrain focal ratio, typically $1/(8 \times 2) = 0.063$ radian, and a collimator is placed between slit and prism so that the light pencil incident upon the latter is parallel. The emergent dispersed, collimated pencils are viewed through a small telescope for spectroscopic purposes. When used as a spectrograph, the eyepiece of the telescope is removed and a photographic plate is inserted at the focal plane of the objective. The scale of the spectrogram so formed is dependent upon the dispersion characteristics of the prism and the focal length of the objective which clearly must be achromatized for as many wavelengths as practicable. Apochromatic triplets, comprising three elements achromatized for three wavelengths, are commonly used. Another way of improvement is to slightly tilt the plate towards the prism at the violet end and away from it at the red end of the spectrum. When it is used as a spectrometer, a hairline graticule is inserted at the focal plane of the objective, so that the dispersed spectrum and the superimposed hairline, set parallel to the slit, are simultaneously in focus to the observer. The prism can be rotated about an axis passing through it and parallel to the slit, by means of a micrometer-type thimble calibrated in wavelengths. Rotation of the prism scans the dispersed spectrum past the graticule and the wavelength of the spectral line coincident with the hairline is read from the thimble.

If the graticule is replaced by a second slit, a single monochromatic line of known wavelength may be isolated. Calibration difficulties arise, however, with the use of a symmetrical triangular prism because minimum deviation is only attained when singly refracted light of the chosen wavelength travels parallel to the face opposite the refracting edge of the prism (fig. 3.15) but in no other case. Prisms can be designed to give constant deviation whatever the wavelength ; the prism is turned so that i_1 and i_2 individually change with wavelength, but the angle between AB and DE (fig. 7.1) is constant. Here (a) shows the 90° deviation Broca prism and (b) the 60° deviation Abbe prism.

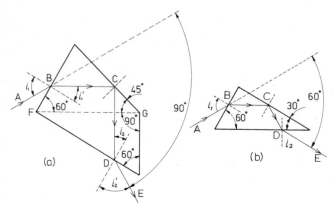

Fig. 7.1. Constant deviation prisms due to (a) Broca and (b) Abbe.

The former is much used in the modern measuring spectrometer. For each wavelength there is an angle of incidence, i_1, of the ray AB for which the singly refracted ray BC lies parallel to the dotted line FG. The direction of the ray is changed through exactly 90° by internal reflection at C and exits from the prism as the ray DE with angle of emergence i_2'. Angles i_1' and i_2 are 30° each and $\sin i_1 = \sin i_2' = n \sin 30° = n/2$. If the ray AB is replaced by a pencil of white light and a small telescope is fixed coaxial with the ray DE, any light emerging from the prism and entering the telescope parallel to its axis must have satisfied the equation $n = 2 \sin i_1 = 2 \sin i_2'$. Rotation of the prism by the calibrated micrometer thimble successively satisfies this requirement for every wavelength present. Thus the selected spectral line may be brought to the centre of the telescope field and so to coincidence with the hairline. It is usual to mount the Broca prism in the spectrometer

126

as in fig. 7.2 which shows the permanent 90° relationship between collimator and telescope. A photographic plate placed in the focal plane of the objective converts the instrument to a spectrograph, when the wavelength micrometer thimble is used to bring the required section of the spectrum on to the plate.

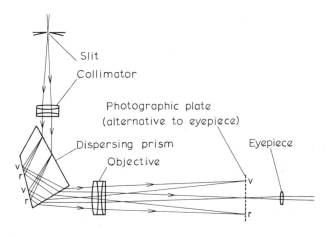

Fig. 7.2. Constant deviation spectroscope.

The prism spectroscope is adequate for most duties extending a little beyond the range of the visible spectrum and the use of a durable glass prism is an advantage. The spectral range may be extended considerably by using prisms of more exotic optical crystals (see Chapter 11) providing that the lenses in the system are similarly special. Most crystals are less durable than glass because in varying degree they are relatively soft, hygroscopic, or less resistant to chemical attack.

7.2. The slitless spectrograph

A very large prism termed the objective prism fulfils a primary function in the slitless spectrograph, which is in effect an adaption of the telescope. Formerly used with photographic refractors, the objective prism is commonly applied to the wide angle, high resolution Schmidt telescopes of today. The prism is mounted in front of the lens or mirror (or in front of the corrector plate in the case of the Schmidt) and, because the image of a star is nominally a point, the image of each star on the photographic plate is spread out by the objective prism into a very thin continuous spectrum, interrupted at the positions where absorption lines would normally occur with a slit spectrograph. During the exposure the telescope is oscillated slightly on one of its axes appropriate to

127

trailing the star image in a direction parallel to the refracting edge of the prism. From this action a widened spectrogram of each star in the field is obtained simultaneously upon the same plate in a single exposure, during which each star image serves as its own slit. The interruptions then show up as absorption lines on the spectrogram of each star. A great deal of work on spectral classification of faint stars is now done with objective prisms.

There are disadvantages, and the main one is that in the large telescope, the stellar images are shimmer discs of appreciable diameter (seeing, Chapter 4) and so the spectra are not so pure nor the lines so sharp as with a slit spectrograph. Another is that no comparison spectra as reference standards for radial velocity measurement can be applied, but this objection can be circumscribed by producing direct and reversed spectra side by side, each having the same dispersion. This is done by rotating the objective prism through exactly 180 degrees between consecutive exposures, but it was not until 1947 that the required combination of extreme mechanical and optical accuracy were attained by C. Fehrenbach in Haute Provence, in the design and construction of his 'normal-field prism.'

7.3. *The grating spectrograph*

The alternative to the prism is the diffraction grating which, in the form of a reflective element, solves the problem of restricted spectral range suffered by the prisms and transmission gratings. Highly specialized echelette reflection gratings have been developed, the general form of which is shown at fig. 7.3. An optically flat glass plate is vacuum-coated on one side with aluminium and this metallic layer is very finely ruled using a diamond-tipped tool to produce a regular array of grooves shaped typically as shown, the reflective face of each groove being optically flat. The grating interval for such an element may be

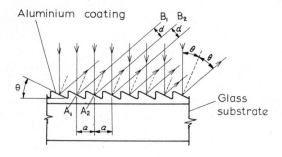

Fig. 7.3. Echelette reflection grating.

less than 1/1200 mm and for a given grating width, the resolving power in a given order, which is proportional to the total number of grooves in use, is inversely proportional to this interval.

If a spectroscope is capable of just resolving two spectral lines of wavelengths λ and $\lambda + \delta\lambda$, the ratio $\lambda/\delta\lambda$ defines the spectroscopic resolving power. A good quality prism spectrometer will usually resolve the sodium doublet D_1 (589·593 nm) and D_2 (588·996 nm), giving resolving power $\lambda/\delta\lambda \approx 1000$. By contrast, a 1200 lines per millimetre echelette grating of width about 20 cm has a theoretical resolving power in the first order ($k = 1$) approaching 50 000. A critical requirement is to maintain uniform spacing of the rulings and the same profile for each. In fig. 7.3 a plane monochromatic wavefront from a collimated slit source is incident upon the grating in a plane A_1, A_2 etc., from which points new wavelets expand with equal amplitudes at equal distances from the points of reflection. Rays reflected from identical points on adjacent rulings thus differ in optical path by an amount $a \sin 2\theta$. Without the shaped grooves assisting, reinforcement occurs if this path difference is $k\lambda$, where k is an integer, but with their help a spectrum is obtained which gives maximum brilliance in a predetermined wavelength which is called the blaze wavelength of the grating. Such a grating can offer the advantages of high resolving power, light concentration in a selected wavelength, and a greatly increased spectral range.

7.4. *The coudé spectrograph*

Of all the spectroscopic equipment, the coudé spectrograph is the largest. An appreciation of its size relative to the telescope is gained from fig. 7.4 (*a*) which is a scale diagram showing the ray path of the 98 inch Isaac Newton Telescope and associated coudé spectrograph at the Royal Greenwich Observatory. This installation is chosen because the spectrograph ray paths are on the plane of the meridian, which means that if the telescope is set at 6 hours H.A. and $+90°$ dec. as shown, the entire ray path from sky to photographic plate may be accurately represented.

The functioning of the coudé spectrograph is dependent upon the ability of the telescope to focus the image of a star at a fixed point in the observatory and from the same direction, regardless of the changing attitude of the telescope during a prolonged period of star tracking.

Starlight incident upon the primary mirror (1) is reflected to incidence upon the secondary mirror (2), which must now be labelled the coudé secondary. The light from here is intercepted by the first coudé flat (3), at the intersection of the polar and declination axes. It

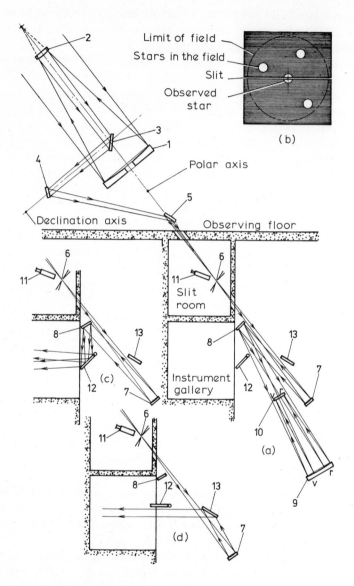

Limit of field
Stars in the field
Slit
Observed
star

(b)

2

3

1

4

5

Polar axis

Declination axis

Observing floor

6

6

11

11

Slit
room

8

13

8

13

12

(c)

7

Instrument
gallery

12

7

10

(a)

6

9

11

8

12

13

(d)

7

Fig. 7.4. Coudé spectrograph and other facilities for the 98 inch telescope of the Royal Greenwich Observatory, Herstmonceux. (a) Coudé ray path in relation to the telescope. (b) Typical star field as seen through the slit viewer. (c) Interception of collimated, dispersed light. (d) Interception of collimated, undispersed light.

130

has a fixed relationship with mirrors 1 and 2, and always reflects the pencil out of the telescope tube through a hollow declination trunnion to incidence upon the second coudé flat (4). The latter is mounted upon the fork and so rotates with the tube about the polar axis, but not about the declination axis. The reflected pencil is thus re-directed back to the polar axis, but now behind the primary mirror, to be intercepted by the third coudé flat (5), sometimes called the fifth mirror. This has fixed relationship with mirror (4), and so rotates with the fork about the polar axis. From mirror (5) the converging pencil is directed through a hole in the observing floor, to focus the star image upon the coudé slit (6) fixed in position in the slit room. Light passing through the slit diverges to incidence upon the collimating mirror (7) which is tilted about an axis perpendicular to the page, to the extent required to reflect the collimated (parallel) pencil to the diffraction grating (8). The latter is a plane, echelette grating (see fig. 7.3) which disperses the polychromatic parallel pencil into a collimated spectrum, (that is to say, every wavelength is reflected as a parallel monochromatic pencil), to incidence upon the camera mirror (9). This mirror is a concave paraboloid which focuses the dispersed pencils as a continuous progression of images of the slit (6) in respective wavelengths upon the curved photographic plate in the plateholder (10).

In order to ensure that the image of the required star really does fall symmetrically upon the slit, the slit jaws have reflecting upper surfaces and are slightly inclined to the normal of the ray path as shown, enabling the reflected field to be observed through the slit viewer (11). This is a small telescope through which the field is seen in relation to the slit, fig. 7.4 (b) ; using this, the large telescope may be guided manually for the last few seconds of arc to attain and then to maintain the observed star image on the coudé slit.

Other apparatus is housed in a small gallery below the slit room into which starlight from the slit may be directed horizontally. In fig. 7.4 (c) the ray path is as described as far as the grating (8) which is rotated anti-clockwise about an axis perpendicular to the page (its scanning axis) until the dispersed pencils meet the flat mirror (12) which reflects the light into the small instrument gallery. In fig. 7.4 (d) the ray path is the same only as far as the collimating mirror (7) which, while being slightly tilted, is mounted in a cell which is coaxial with the polar axis of the telescope. Rotation of the cell through 180° about this axis reflects the collimated pencil, not to the grating (8) as before, but to a fixed flat mirror (13) which directs the undispersed pencil horizontally into the instrument gallery for purposes which require ordinary light. The mirror (12) is raised by rotation about the hinge at one edge, to allow the undispersed pencil through to the gallery.   All these movements are power-driven and remotely controlled.   While a spectrogram is being exposed, or minimal light level experiments are being conducted, nobody is in the great spectrograph chamber which is, in effect, the interior of an uncommonly large camera in which there is total darkness (apart from the subject light).

A typical diffraction grating for this spectrograph measures 20×25 cm and is ruled with 1200 lines per millimetre.   Such a grating, intended for optimum photographic performance, is designed for a blaze wavelength of 410 nm, that is, in the blue.   The wavelength scale is 0.24 nm per millimetre of spectrogram length on a photographic plate 2.5 cm wide $\times 50$ cm long.   The entire visible spectrum at this scale cannot be received upon a plate of this length, but it can be built up from several exposures made with the grating rotated about its scanning axis to reflect sections of the spectrum in turn on to the camera mirror.   Thus, the letters r and v at mirror (9) and plate (10) in fig. 7.4 (a) refer to the directions of the red and violet ends of the spectrum, not necessarily to the actual wavelengths.

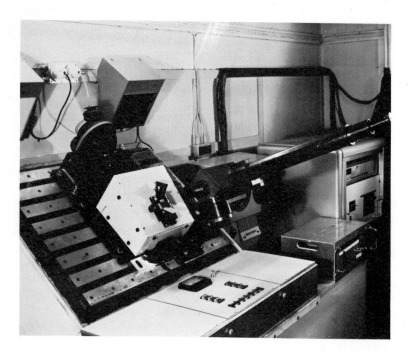

Fig. 7.5.   Coudé slit and slit viewer.   *Royal Greenwich Observatory, Herstmonceux.*

Fig. 7.5 is a photograph of the coudé slit (mounted upon the white box) and the slit viewer. The slotted table is the upper terminal component of the spectrograph structure and the slit room is built around it. The table is ' squared on ', that is, set on a plane perpendicular to the polar axis of the main telescope and the tilt of the slit can be seen. Light from the main telescope enters the slit room from the top right hand corner of the photograph and focuses upon the slit. A further coudé slit viewer may be seen at the base of the polar shaft of the 48 inch Canadian telescope (fig. 5.4) and the horizontal coudé ray path for the same instrument is shown in fig. 8.3.

7.5. Interpreting the spectrum

Figure 7.6 shows a spectrogram of the sun, produced by the Royal Greenwich Observatory, for the spectral bandwidth 395 to 445 nm. It is overlaid for comparison, by the spectrogram of an electric arc struck between iron electrodes in an argon atmosphere. Note that the continuous solar spectrum produced by the hot material at lower levels is crossed by dark absorption lines caused by the intervening presence of the cooler outer layers, and that the comparison spectrum is composed wholly of bright lines, arising mainly from the vaporization of the iron electrodes and the hot argon arc shield. It is interesting to note that even in a laboratory controlled atmosphere of ' pure ' iron vapour and argon, some impurities creep in, for at least two lines of hydrogen, at 410·1 and 434 nm are present in the comparison spectrum. They are much more strongly present in the Sun's spectrum due to hydrogen abundance.

One may thus conclude that iron is present in the Sun, because the bright emission of iron lines in the laboratory comparison exactly match a similar set of absorption lines in the solar spectrum. It can also be deduced that there is no appreciable radial velocity between the Earth and the Sun because there is no Doppler shift between the bright and dark line spectra from its centre, and that the temperature of the material producing the *continuous* spectrum is lower than that of a body whose peak is within the bandwidth of the spectrogram because the spectrum is seen to be brighter at the right-hand end where the wavelength is greatest. Continuation of fig. 7.6 to the right would show peak emission at about 500 nm, which by Wien's displacement law indicates a solar temperature near the surface of $2898 \times 10^3/500 = 5800$ K. (See the Planck distribution curves of fig. 3.1)

Any source showing an appreciable Doppler shift in its spectrogram has a considerable velocity relative to the observer along the

Fig. 7.6. Solar spectrogram with iron/argon comparison. *Royal Greenwich Observatory, Herstmonceux.*

134

line of sight, for whilst the velocity of light in vacuo is constant, regardless of the relative velocity of source and observer (Einstein, 1905) wavelength is not. If source and observer have no relative velocity, $\nu\lambda = c$ where ν is frequency, λ is wavelength and c is the velocity of light $\approx 3 \times 10^8$ m s^{-1}. In a time interval t, the emitted ray occupies a length $\nu\lambda t$ increasing to $\nu\lambda t + vt$ if there is a relative velocity of recession v between source and observer, in which case the same number of waves are stretched over a greater length and an increase in wavelength is observed.* If the new wavelength is λ_1 then

$$\nu t\lambda_1 = \nu t\lambda + vt$$

$$\therefore \lambda_1 = \lambda + (v/\nu) = \lambda[1 + (v/c)] \tag{7.1}$$

If the change in wavelength $(\lambda_1 - \lambda)$ is called $\Delta\lambda$, eqn. 7.1 becomes

$$\Delta\lambda/\lambda = v/c \tag{7.2}$$

Taking a numerical example, the H$_\alpha$ emission line of hydrogen has a wavelength of 656·3 nm. Suppose that a stellar spectrogram shows the H$_\alpha$ absorption line as having a wavelength of 656·4 nm, then

$$v = (656\cdot4 - 656\cdot3) \times 3 \times 10^8/656\cdot3 = 46 \times 10^3 \text{ m s}^{-1}$$

as the velocity of recession of the star along the line of sight of the observer.

So the extent of the Doppler shift, or even the complete lack of it, gives useful information. We saw (Chapter 2) that telluric lines gave early astrophysicists a lot of trouble. They are now readily recognized for many reasons, one of which is the complete absence of Doppler shift, because the Earthbound atmosphere which produces them has no significant radial velocity relative to the spectrograph. The telluric lines are mainly due to molecules and are so identified (Chapter 3). The telluric lines are now very accurately catalogued and so their position on the spectrogram is known precisely.

Spectrograms of the eastern and western limbs of the Sun (the visible edges of the photosphere), overlaid by suitable comparison spectra, show its angular velocity of rotation more accurately than observation of the movement of such transient surface phenomena as sunspots across the disc. The Eastern limb at the solar equator has a relative velocity of approach of about 2 km s^{-1} which shows as a Doppler shift towards the blue, and the velocity of recession at the Western limb

---

* This is the conventional treatment which assumes that light travels through a stationary medium. But see standard textbooks such as *Light* by R. W. Ditchburn (Blackie & Co.).

produces a similar shift towards the red. Spectrograms of the limbs progressively nearer to the solar poles show, with decreasing accuracy due to the reducing *linear* velocity, that the *angular* velocity is about $3 \cdot 34$ μrad s^{-1} at the equator and about $2 \cdot 42$ μrad s^{-1} at 75° solar latitude, so that the Sun is rotating as a *fluid* mass.

Beyond the confines of the solar system, many of the naked eye stars are, in fact, binary systems, that is, two stars in orbit about a common mass centre. The telescope will resolve many of them into separate components, but there is a further class, termed spectroscopic binaries for which separation is beyond the resolving power of the largest telescope, due to great distance of the pair or to extreme proximity of the stellar components. If the orbital plane is such as to produce substantial velocity of the components along the line of sight of the observer, the spectrograph will detect the presence of two stars in a single image, focused upon the slit.

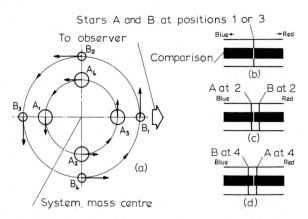

Fig. 7.7. Detection of a spectroscopic binary star. (a) Geometry of the two-star system. (b) Spectrogram of both stars moving across the line of sight. (c) Star A approaching, star B receding. (d) Star A receding, star B approaching.

Figure 7.7 (*a*) is a schematic diagram of such a binary pair, star A having greater mass than star B, so accounting for the difference in orbit radius about the system's mass centre. The subscripts 1 to 4 indicate progressive positions of the binary pair during one complete orbit and linear velocity vectors are also shown. The result on the spectrogram is more clearly shown as a drawing than as a photograph and one spectral line only is used to illustrate an exaggeration of the Doppler shift. In fig. 7.7 (*b*) the absorption and comparison lines are exactly

136

aligned, implying that the image on the slit is of either a single star with no radial velocity or a binary system orientated as at subscripts 1 or 3. In fig. 7.7 (c) the absorption line has divided, so establishing the latter proposition. The line from star A has shifted a shorter distance towards the blue than the line from star B has shifted towards the red and in fig. 7.7 (d) the condition is reversed, confirming the presence of a spectroscopic binary. The wavelength differences are measured either by examination of the spectrogram with a traversing microscope or, more accurately, by comparing the comparison and absorption lines interferometrically. The change of wavelength leads to the magnitude of the linear velocity vectors for each star, and by accurate timing of the period one can then find the common orbital angular velocity of the system. So the orbital radius and hence the mass of each star may be calculated.*

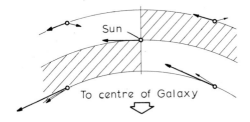

Fig. 7.8. Spectroscopic analysis of galactic structure.

In a wider sense still, the Doppler shift has revealed much about the structure of the Galaxy. If the assumption is made that gravity is universal and that therefore the stars tend to rotate orbitally around the galactic nucleus like the planets of the solar system around the Sun, those nearer the centre will have higher linear velocity than those nearer the periphery. Figure 7.8 is a highly regularized diagram of four stars in a part of the Galaxy which contains the Sun. All five bodies have galactic orbital velocity vectors shown in heavy line and resultant radial velocity vectors relative to the Sun in finer line. Thus, one may expect stars in the hatched and clear quadrants to show apparent velocities of recession and approach respectively. Large numbers of stars in each quadrant show Doppler shifts that confirm this supposition.

* It is not possible to determine the masses of the components of a spectroscopic binary unless we know the inclination of the system. The inclination cannot be found from the spectral line shifts alone since these give the component of the velocity in the line of sight. If the system is an eclipsing binary as well, then we can obtain the inclination and hence the masses of the stars.

On the grandest scale of all, the evidence for the ' expanding universe ' rests on Doppler shift observation which indicate an apparent velocity of recession near to $0 \cdot 8c$ for objects at the extreme range of the largest telescopes ; although velocity alone is looked upon with great suspicion by modern astronomers, as the sole reason for the undisputed reddening of light from sources at the distant reaches of the universe.

7.6. *Image slicing*

Loss of light at the spectrograph slit is serious although quite normal. Figure 7.4 (*b*) shows the reason, for that part of the star image which falls *upon* the slit jaws clearly does not pass *through* them. Very successful improvements to coudé spectrograph performance have been achieved at the Dominion Astrophysical Observatory, Victoria, B.C., by application

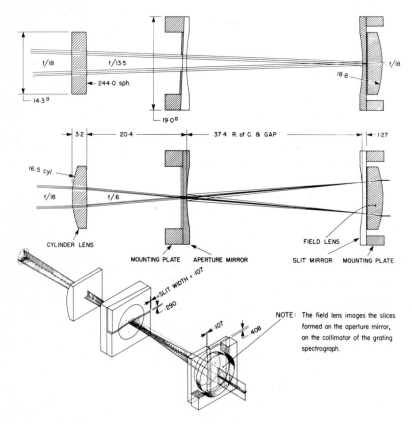

Fig. 7.9.   Victoria-type superpositioning image slicer.   *Dominion Astrophysical Observatory, Victoria, B.C.*

138

of high reflectance coatings (Chapter 4) supplemented by the development of the superpositioning image slicer. The essentials of this are shown in fig. 7.9, arranged for a horizontal axis spectrograph with vertical entrance slit which the image slicer replaces.

Starlight enters the image slicer through the cylindrical lens which is weakly spherical on its exit surface. Two line images are thus produced, a horizontal one passing through the division separating the halves of the aperture mirror and a vertical one which coincides with the spectrograph slit—that is, the division separating the halves of the slit mirror. The facing aperture and slit mirrors are separated by their common radius of curvature, the centres of which are in such positions upon the surface of the mirror opposite, (on the edges of the respective

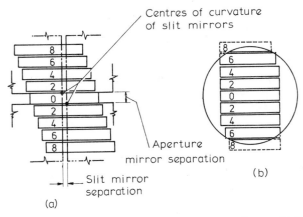

Fig. 7.10. Stack of light slices produced by the image slicer. (a) Stack projected onto the aperture mirror, and (b) onto the spectrograph collimator mirror. The numeral shown in each slice denotes the number of reflections to which the slice has been subjected. *Adapted from data supplied by the Dominion Astrophysical Observatory, Victoria, B.C.*

dividing slits in fact), that light which falls upon the slit mirror surface is reflected back to the aperture mirror. From here, it is redirected to the slit mirror, displaced from its original position to the extent that a slice of the returned image passes through the slit. Repeated reflections between the aperture and slit mirrors result in the eventual passage of the entire image, cut into slit-width slices. Thus the losses are restricted to those arising from two fairly thin lenses and from multiple reflections which, in the case of the Victoria instruments are low, because of multi-layer high reflectance coatings on all but the telescope primary mirror. Figure 7.10 shows a stack of slices as they appear (*a*) on the image slicer aperture mirror and (*b*) on the spectrograph collimator. The 'skewness' of the stack disappears after passage through the slit and the field lens.

Figures 7.9 and 7.10 relate to an instrument designed to work with the 72 inch telescope of the DAO but similar equipment applied to the 48 inch telescope has raised its spectrographic camera speed at least to parity with that of the 200 inch Palomar telescope when working a conventional slit in the blue region with a grating dispersion of 0·65 nm/mm, and to better than this with a grating dispersion of 0·24 nm/mm. The 200 inch remains unchallenged outside this limited but important field.

7.7. *Interferometry*

Stellar interferometry began with the achievement of A. A. Michelson who in 1920 sought, with some success, to measure indirectly the diameter of the bright red star Betelgeuse. Using the exceptionally rigid 100 inch telescope of Mount Wilson Observatory, he mounted a structural beam across the top end, to which he attached four plane mirrors as in fig. 7.11. The outer mirrors, each placed at a distance *s*, about 120 inches from the optical axis of the telescope, extended the effective aperture (for this purpose) to 240 inches; the other two mirrors, each 22·5 inches from the optical axis, redirected the starlight down the tube in the normal manner. Each of the outer mirrors can be regarded as a slit, so that the pattern in the focal plane is really a two-slit interference pattern.

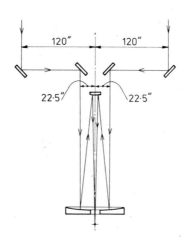

Fig. 7.11. Stellar interferometer applied to the 100 inch telescope of Mount Wilson Observatory.

The theory, as given in Michelson's *Studies in Optics*, Chapter 9, shows that this pattern disappears where the angle subtended at the outer mirrors by a stellar source is $\Delta\theta = \frac{1}{2}(1\cdot22\lambda/\alpha) = 1\cdot22\lambda/s$. To measure $\Delta\theta$ then, s is adjusted until the interference pattern vanishes for light of wavelength λ. Michelson there mentions Betelgeuse, for which $s = 3\cdot065$ m at $\lambda = 575$ nm, which gives $\Delta\theta$ as $0\cdot047$ arc seconds. This is the angular diameter of the star. Some accounts of the Michelson interferometer show two actual slits, closer together than the objective aperture ; Michelson mentions this stage in the development of the instrument, as used on a 12-inch telescope to measure the diameter of the larger satellites of Jupiter, of the order of 1 arc second—so that s had to be only about 15 cm.

The name interferometer means an instrument which uses wave interference for making measurements. It may be used for measuring wavelengths in terms of distances observed within the apparatus, or for measuring distances in terms of known wavelengths—hence, for example, the definition of the metre in terms of the wavelength of a line in the spectrum of ^{86}Kr. The Michelson interferometer is shown in principle in fig. 7.12. Light from source S is transmitted through the

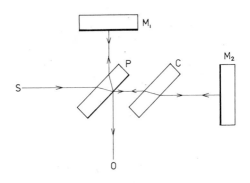

Fig. 7.12.   Principle of Michelson's interferometer.

flat glass plate P which is semi-aluminized on its back surface to reflect part of the incident flux to the mirror M_1 whence it returns through P to the observer at O. The unreflected part of the original ray is transmitted through the compensating glass flat C (which is cut from the same piece of material as P but has no reflective coating) to the mirror M_2, whence it is returned to P, where it is superposed on the beam from M_1, with a difference in optical path. This difference may be varied by micrometer adjustment of M_1 along the light path, a half wavelength movement bringing about a whole wavelength change to the path length, so producing one complete fringe cycle.

The Fabry-Pérot interferometer has two parallel glass plates, the surfaces of which are set perpendicular to the light path. The facing surfaces are aluminized to about 20 per cent transmission. The glass plates are called an étalon and may be separated by micrometer adjustment with a result similar to that with the Michelson interferometer except that multiple reflections within the étalon sharpen the fringes. Increasing the plate separation also increases the resolving power but decreases the spectral range, a drawback which may be overcome by placing a second étalon of small, fixed separation in tandem with the original one. Then we obtain the resolving power of the larger spacing and the range of the smaller spacing.

Under favourable conditions and in selected regions of the visible spectrum, mainly at the short wave end, interferometric methods can be used to measure wavelength differences as small as 0·1 pm.

Interference is also applied in the design of the modern multilayer optical filter, the forerunners of which were the monochromatic filters produced at the Observatoire du Pic-du-Midi by B. Lyot in 1933, which have transmission bandwidths as narrow as 0·07 nm. Today, interference filters are commercially available to cover the whole range of visible wavelengths and which extend far into the infrared. The filters consist of stacks of thin films of transparent materials of different refractive indices deposited upon a substrate. Light is reflected at each interface and is superposed upon that reflected from the other interfaces, interfering constructively for some wavelengths (giving high reflectance) and interfering destructively for others (giving high transmittance). Optical path length and equivalent refractive index vary with the angle of incidence and because of this, the focal ratio of the normally incident pencil is limited by transmission bandwith because the peripheral rays of a non-parallel pencil are inclined to the pencil axis. Thus an $f/3$ pencil acceptable to a bandpass filter, say 50 to 60 nm wide, would need to be altered to about $f/11$ or $f/12$ if it were to be used with a narrow band filter, say 1 nm wide. Some of the many materials used for such filters are the dielectrics zinc sulphide, magnesium fluoride and silicon dioxide and the conductors aluminium, nickel and copper, all deposited as films of transparent thinness.

7.8. *Photometry*

The items of equipment designed to supplement the telescope are mostly specially designed for a particular requirement and the photograph fig. 7.13 shows such an assembly mounted at the Cassegrain

Fig. 7.13. Detail of the Cassegrain observing station of the 98 inch telescope of RGO. *Royal Greenwich Observatory, Herstmonceux.*

focus of the 98 inch telescope of the Royal Greenwich Observatory. It is a two star photometer, designed for the purpose of making simultaneous photometric measurements of two stars in the same field so that inaccuracies due to thin cloud and poor seeing apply equally to both stars and the comparison is truer. Both photometers are mounted on their own XY axis slideways, the whole being attached to the permanent Cassegrain turntable which is standard equipment on any large telescope. The photometers can be traversed to positions in the field

143

where the images of the selected stars fall upon the photometric sensors.

Although the specialized equipment is usually custom-built, the principles employed may be categorized and the following sums up the important facilities presently available. The fundamental parameter in stellar photometry is magnitude. Until about 1950, one of the simple but imperfect systems of magnitude used by many astronomers was divided into three sections, VPB (Visual, Photographic and Bolometric), which accommodated the sensitivities of the separate receptors, as the names imply. All three are based on the logarithmic Pogson scale in which five magnitudes span a brightness range of 100 to 1. Thus, if two stars differ by one magnitude, the common logarithm of the ratio of the quantities of light received by the receptor is 0·4, that is, the ratio of the light received is 2·512 : 1 (the antilog of 0·4). Magnitude systems rest upon the selection of certain stars of standard brightness (and similar laboratory calibrated standards), the original being the bright star Vega in the constellation Lyra which was assigned zero visual magnitude. By today's standards of measurement, it is very nearly so. The Pogson scale is most useful because if a selection of standard sources have had their magnitudes measured by a reference system, these sources may be re-measured by a given photometer and a factor established to convert the ' natural ' sensitivity of the photometer into reference system calibration.

The older magnitude systems were finally put aside in favour of the UBV (Ultraviolet, Blue and Visual) system, still based on the Pogson scale, established by H. L. Johnson and W. W. Morgan in 1953, and which is now internationally recognized as the standard reference system for wide band photometry in the visual and photographic regions of the spectrum. B magnitudes are, in effect, photographic wavelengths with most of the ultraviolet excluded from the measurement, and the combined range of B and V is therefore an index of colour. Other systems have been established in the longer wavelengths including infrared, with a variety of intermediate and narrow bandwidths, the edges of which are sometimes rather difficult to define. One system of magnitude—bolometric—may be very firmly defined but here, the difficulty lies in measurement. According to Sir Arthur Eddington's definition, bolometric values are those arising from the total of radiation regardless of wavelength, received at the top of the Earth's atmosphere. But to be practical at the telescope, that means the total radiation which can be intercepted and measured in the observatory.

In the narrower bandwidths, the differences in magnitudes in relation to the colour indices of the stars when a natural* and a reference system

* Natural to the characteristics of a specific photometer.

are compared is called a colour equation. Stars of the same colour index do not always have the same Planck distribution, so when two magnitude systems are similar and the colour equation is small, the difference is given by a linear equation. The colour equation allows conversion of the observed magnitudes into the reference system so that the work of one astronomer may be correlated to that of another, anywhere in the world and without regard to the equipment used except to quote the colour equation. It is also the simplest way to define the colour of a magnitude system.

So much for system, now to the equipment. Starting from the simplest standpoint, the practised eye, while poor at assessing absolute brightness, is very good at comparing luminance and is sensitive to differences of about 0·1 magnitude. With the advent of photography by Louis Daguerre in 1839 a course was set for improvement in photometry, but stellar photography had to wait until 1852 for the collodion plate. Photographic photometry has since developed into a cheap, quick and fairly accurate method, especially for large quantity surveys.

The basic instrument used is the iris photometer which measures the amount of light passing through an aperture from a reference source. The exposed plate is placed in position so that the image of the star to be measured photometrically is central on the aperture with a nominal annulus of transparent plate around it. (The star image is dense, the sky background transparent). Although the true image size of a point-source star is the same regardless of its brightness, the photographed image for a given exposure time varies in size and density, depending upon the object's brightness, due to the integration of incident radiation during exposure and the effect of multiple reflections within the thickness of the gelatin matrix which carries the light-sensitive chemicals. Thus the image of a bright star is larger and denser and obscures more of the reference light passing through the aperture than does a faint star. Variations in plate response make it essential to calibrate each plate by including standard stars (real or artificial) in the same brightness range, at the same exposure. Photo-emulsions are sensitive to a range of wavelengths, from the shortest waves which reach the ground to the near infrared at about 1200 nm.

7.9. Photoelectric photometry

In photoelectric photometry, the instrument has a small aperture through which starlight converges from the telescope secondary mirror, and a retractable prism which is placed in the optical path to allow eyepiece viewing of the field so that the required star image can be guided to the photometer aperture. It is the image of the aperture, including that of the star, which is focused upon the photoelectric cell (photocell). The photocells used for this work are either photoemissive, or photoconductive (using semiconductors) in which illumination of the cell causes a change in the electrical resistance because the energy gap, a fraction of an electron volt, is well in the infrared).

At the low flux intensity levels encountered in stellar photometry, the current flowing in the external circuit of a photoemissive cell is proportional to the illumination of the cathode for light of a given wavelength, but it is not equally sensitive to a similar intensity in different wavelengths. It is thus usual to employ one or more filters in the system which, in conjunction with the characteristics of the cathode material define the effective bandwidth, or to pass the starlight through a grating monochromator which has the same effect without incurring transmission losses. Thus, for the star under observations a record of photometric values is obtained for its component wavelengths.

For stars of brightness sufficient to produce a significant signal against the background sky radiation, the photoelectric photometer has the advantage of producing an instant result, either on a meter or directly on a chart which is a permanent record, of luminance in a whole range of wavelengths if the spectrum is scanned across the entrance aperture. The equipment must be calibrated for this purpose and amplification of the received signal up to 10^{14} is required to provide the few milliamperes required to drive the recording pen. Since the mid 1930's development of the photomultiplier has enabled such enormous gains to be made. In the multiplier phototube, upwards of nine multiplying surfaces are arranged in cascade, a hit by one photoelectron on the first surface releasing three or four secondary electrons which are further multiplied at the second surface, and so on. Gains up to 10^6 in the multiplier are normal, after which valve (more recently, transistor) amplification does not add excessive electrical noise.

Of the many cathode materials available for photoemissive cells, potassium hydride is sensitive to a narrow band in the blue/violet region ; caesium oxide has a greater bandwidth with peak response in the near infrared.

The caesium/antimony cathode, discovered in 1938 and widely used today, greatly improved detection of radiation in a bandwidth from ultraviolet to yellow, with peak output in the blue/violet, in which region one incident photon causes the emission of one electron. With semiconductor photoconductive materials, in which a reduction in resistance has to be measured, the chief problem is thermal noise in the detector itself. At 300 K (about room temperature), the peak of black body emission is about 10 μm which means that incident radiation is competing hopelessly against detector noise. The solution is to cool the receiving photocell to a temperature at which, by Wien's displacement law, the peak of thermal emission within the cell is far beyond the wavelength of incident radiation. Intrinsic indium antimonide (InSb) can work effectively at temperatures as high as 150 K, and gold-doped germanium has maximum sensitivity at 65 K. Practical considerations govern cell cooling however and liquefied gases at atmospheric pressure, notably nitrogen (77 K), hydrogen (at 20 K) and helium (at 4 K) are frequently used.

It is difficult to discriminate between the emission from the faint stars and that of the sky background because the noise equivalent power (NEP) of the cell, even when it is cooled, often exceeds that of the star signal. Optical chopping can overcome this difficulty. Somewhere in the ray path, a small mirror or prism is oscillated at small amplitude and with a frequency of around 60 Hz so that the image of the aperture focused upon the cathode contains alternately sky signal and sky-plus-star signal, the former carrying slightly less energy than the latter. Instant readout is not available with this method because the energy is so low that separate integration (using capacitors) of the photomultiplier output from alternations extending over a period of an hour or more is needed to accumulate a reliable difference between the two. The faintest stars are measured in a wide bandwidth because a very faint monochromatic line is too weak to stimulate the most sensitive cathode. Locating the faint star within the entrance aperture presents some difficulty because many are too dim to be seen by eye, even through the telescope. The technique used to locate them is to set up the images of two brighter stars in the same field to co-ordinated positions on the image plane when it is known that the co-ordinates for the invisible object will intercept the aperture. Prolonged exposure photographs of the star field taken previously through the same telescope are used to establish the co-ordinates.

7.10. *The bolometer*

Bolometric measurements add to visual and photometric results, the energy-flux carried by all the other wavelengths that can penetrate the atmosphere, which means mainly the infrared. The presence of infrared radiation beyond the red end of the visible solar spectrum was discovered by Sir William Herschel who, in 1800, noted an increase in indicated temperature when the blackened bulb of a thermometer was placed in that position. Sir William Huggins in 1868 improved sensitivity sufficiently to detect readings from stellar spectra using a bismuth–antimony thermocouple junction and so started a process of development

147

which culminated (1960) in the liquid helium cooled germanium bolometer due to F. J. Low, which approaches the limit to the exchange of quanta between receptor and its environment. Between these two extremes, many developments and discoveries have provided a variety of equipment. A number of thermocouples arranged in series so that one set of junctions occupies a narrow strip suitable for intercepting infrared spectral lines is termed a linear thermopile. Sensitivity up to 80 μV per μW of incident radiation may be obtained by mounting the linear thermopile in a high vacuum.

A simple bolometer takes the form of a narrow platinum foil ribbon, mounted zig-zag fashion upon a glass substrate and blackened to improve its energy absorption. Incident radiation causes a temperature rise in the metal and a resulting increase in resistance which may be measured in a bridge circuit.

The thermistor (thermally sensitive resistor), is a bolometer developed from solid state electronics. Two small flakes of semiconducting material about 10 μm thick are blackened to absorb radiation well, and are fixed to a heat sink in an evacuated housing which has an infrared-transmitting window. One flake is exposed, the other is to compensate for changes in the ambient temperature and so is shielded from radiation. Both matched flakes form the adjacent arms of a bridge circuit. When radiation falls upon the active flake the bridge is unbalanced and the off-balance potential difference detected.

The Golay pneumatic cell is ' read ' by a conventional photoemissive cell excited by a source lamp, but the unique feature is the modulation of this exciting beam. Radiation enters the cell axially through a tiny cylindrical chamber a few millimetres long and about 1·5 mm in diameter. The entry end of the chamber has a transmitting window behind which is mounted an energy-absorbing film of low thermal capacity. The exit end is closed by a flexible membrane the outer surface of which is coated with an evaporated metallic mirror finish. The chamber is filled with xenon gas, the pressure of which increases when it is heated by energy absorbed as infrared radiation which is then dissipated into the gas by the thermal absorption film. The curvature of the flexible mirror depends on the gas pressure and so represents the energy received. The exciter lamp beam is passed through an optical system of which the flexible mirror is a part, and so arrives at the photoelectric cell with an intensity that depends on the mirror curvature. The Golay cell is used widely in infrared spectroscopy because of its high response right through the infrared spectrum, and even into the short end of the microwaves. In ground-based astronomy it is limited, like any other cell, by the atmospheric windows.

CHAPTER 8
observatory sites and buildings

8.1. *The economics of site selection*

IN the early days of telescope astronomy, observatory site selection was largely a matter of expedience, and the design of the buildings was little removed from the conventional practice of the period. The arrangement was satisfactory because the performance of the equipment, small and sometimes imperfect by present-day standards, was not seriously degraded by the environment. With the increased size and improved accuracy of later telescopes, the atmospheric effects causing poor seeing became troublesome and the inadequacy of conventional buildings became apparent with the demand for a rotatable dome. Even so, right up to the late 1960's, most large telescopes were installed at sites in the countries of origin regardless of their suitability. It is true that observatory buildings had become highly specialized, but those countries which were active in astronomy and which included first-rate observing sites within their boundaries were fortunate and few. But by this time, the groundwork was being laid for the most ambitious telescope building programme in history, many of the dozen or more large instruments then planned to operate in the 1970's being of 3·5 m to 4 m aperture.

A 3·8 m installed telescope carries an estimated capital investment at 1970 values of not less than M£4·8 sterling and few single authorities are willing to bear such cost. Thus, we have the jointly developed instrument of the Anglo-Australian Telescope Project (AAT), and that of the European Southern Observatory (ESO), the latter being a consortium conducting research at a level beyond the scope of a single institution. The instrument of the Kitt Peak National Observatory (KPNO) and that of the Cerro Tolo Inter-American Observatory (CTIO) are being administered and operated by a large group of American universities, the Association of Universities for Research in Astronomy (AURA) and so on. There is thus a total investment approaching, perhaps even exceeding, M£60 and at this level of expenditure, national pride has, with few exceptions, been abandoned in favour of selecting the best accessible sites in the world. This is of crucial importance because an ill-chosen site could drastically reduce the annual observing time relative to that available at the best sites, an important side effect being proportional increase in the hourly cost of observing. In addition, the prevailing seeing may so degrade the performance of, let us say, a 3·5 m telescope that an instrument of considerably smaller aperture at a better site would perform equally well, in which case a large part of the capital investment would be wasted at the poor site.

An extra benefit arising from this more enlightened outlook is the projected distribution of a number of very large telescopes in the southern hemisphere by controlling institutions based north of the equator. For example, the 3·6 m telescope of ESO is being developed at CERN, Geneva, from headquarters in Hamburg, for site installation on Cerro La Silla, about 600 km north of Santiago in the Chilean Andes. Chile will be well endowed with large telescopes by early 1980 due to the eminent suitability of several high altitude sites which were approved by painstaking geographical, meteorological and optical site surveys carried out mainly in the 1960's. At the time of writing the largest telescopes in the southern hemisphere are the 74 inch Radcliffe reflector at Pretoria and the telescope of similar aperture at Mount Stromlo, Australia. Installation of several instruments exceeding twice this aperture during the next few years will do as much to open up the southern sky as the 200 inch of Palomar did in the north, thirty years earlier.

8.2. *Choosing the site*

The most common site requirement for an observatory operating a large modern telescope is high altitude. Many are even now located between 2000 m and 3000 m above sea level and many more will join them at these altitudes in the near future. 3000 m represents a very small percentage of the thickness of the Earth's atmosphere but in certain locations (and this is the kernel of site selection), many of the worst features giving rise to poor seeing and light absorption result from atmospheric effects below this level. Of these areas, some will offer no possibility of gaining access to the site with heavy equipment, but in this respect formidable access difficulties are accepted for the reward of a very good site. The photograph of fig. 8.1 shows the Observatoire du Pic-du-Midi 2830 m above sea level in the French Pyrenées to prove the point. Founded by Bernard Lyot of the Observatoire de Meudon in 1930, it provided the quiet seeing he needed to develop the coronagraph (fig. 2.6).

Of recent years large scale preliminary site survey work has been valuably assisted by orbiting satellite photography. This reveals, among much else, the weather pattern tendencies relative to the terrain

Fig. 8.1. Observatoire du Pic-du-Midi in winter. *Observatoire du Pic-du-Midi.*

and so reduces the time and effort required for a ground based survey. When large scale work is completed, a few sites are isolated and detailed investigation of each is then mounted, extending in some cases over a period of several years before a decision is taken to commit the telescope. Brief examination of an example or two will afford a realistic appraisal of the procedures.

In 1969 the largest active telescopes controlled by the Federal Republic of Germany were (and still are) of 1 m aperture and the Max Planck Institut für Astronomie (MPIA) was set up to improve this situation. Among other instruments, two similar telescopes of 2·2 m aperture are to be installed, one in the northern and one in the southern hemisphere. The northern observatory has been chosen with satellite assistance, at an altitude of 2168 m on the Calar Alto mountain of the Sierra de los Filabres in Almeria, Spain, where 1800 annual hours of observing time are assessed. The southern observatory will be either at Cerro La Silla, Chile, (the ESO choice) or on the Gamsberg plateau 120 km SW of Windhoek in South West Africa where the average night temperature amplitude 2 m above ground is 3·2°C measured over 100 nights, the daily maximum temperature difference is only 11°C and 225 photometric nights are expected annually.

Two photoelectric seeing monitors, small, portable telescopes with a photometric measuring facility, were simultaneously calibrated on the same star at Calar Alto and were then put to work at La Silla and Gamsberg respectively. Early results of these trials are shown in fig. 8.2. where the seeing (assigned the symbol σ) is the r.m.s. image amplitude in arc seconds. The frequency mentioned in the legend and relating to the y axis, refers to the percentage of nights when the seeing was as shown and not to the frequency of image oscillation. The upper part of fig. 8.2 shows that high quality images ($\sigma < 0·4$ arc seconds) are more frequent in South West Africa than in Chile but the distribution of σ values is wider. Photographic trials are also being conducted at both sites by trailing star images across the plate and measuring the deviation. Whilst photographic accuracy is reduced when the seeing is at its best, the results (which could have been disturbingly different) are in fact in accord with the photocell result to within about 0·1 arc second.

A further example concerns an eight-year search by the Carnegie Institution (U.S.A.) for a southern hemisphere site for an observatory mounting a 40 inch reflector which is operating at the present time, a 100 inch scheduled for the end of 1975 and a 200 inch which is part of a more distant programme. If any incentive to even greater care in site selection was needed, it was provided by the projected construction of the world's second 200 inch telescope. The search began in 1963 and

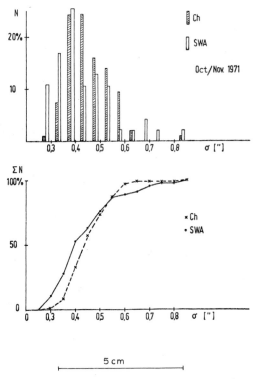

Fig. 8.2. Frequency of seeing, σ, on Gamsberg, South West Africa, and La Silla, Chile, according to photoelectric measurements. $\sigma = $ r.m.s. amplitude of image motion in arc seconds.   The lower part shows cumulative distribution.   *Max Planck Institut für Astronomie, Heidelberg.*

ranged over New Zealand, Australia and Chile, concluding in 1971 with the announcement that the Carnegie Southern Observatory (CARSO) would be at Cerro Las Campanas, Chile.   To assist in implementing the survey programme, four portable 8 inch seeing monitors, similar in purpose to the monitors of the MPIA were built, and three of them were continuously operated for some years at the Carnegie sites, the fourth being operated by ESO on La Silla.

The only result which need concern us from this protracted exercise is that the average seeing at Las Campanas turns out to be 0·85 arc seconds, with best periods at 0·3 arc seconds.   These very low values are attributed in part to the unique topography of the surroundings. Las Campanas, at 2220 m altitude is situated on the northern end of a mountain ridge, so there are no other high mountains for a great distance to the north.   The prevailing night breeze is also from the north and is thus relatively free from turbulence as it blows unimpeded towards and over the site. There is always some anxiety attending the responsibility for site approval, for however exhaustive the seeing trials may be, a portable 20 cm telescope a metre or so above ground does not perform like a 3·5 m telescope 25 metres above ground. The small one can only provide guidance on a parameter (seeing) which is difficult to measure in any case.

There is one modern permanent telescope, however, which approaches the scale of site survey equipment more closely. It is a 24 inch reflector built by Ealing Beck Ltd., of Watford, for the University of Denver which is installed with its declination axis only two or three metres above ground on Mount Evans in the Rocky Mountains near Denver, Colorado. The modest dimensions are the price to be paid for installation at this site which, at an altitude of 4350 m, distinguishes the instrument as the highest ground-based telescope in the world. It is intended to carry out infrared astronomy at this observatory, and in this spectral region the reduced amount of precipitable water vapour remaining above the telescope is a significant advantage.

Weather conditions at the site can be severe and the small 5·5 m diameter dome is designed to withstand wind velocity up to $250\,km\,h^{-1}$. No observing takes place in these conditions of course, but the telescope and its associated equipment can be operated at temperatures down to $-30°C$. At this altitude there are no residential facilities and staffing as required will be arranged from the Echo Lake High Altitude Observatory, 22 km distant and 1430 m below the Mount Evans site. It is possible, although not scheduled at present, that the small telescope may be remotely controlled by cable links from Echo Lake and electronic equipment already installed would assist this development.

8.3. *Buildings and services*

One of the earliest parameters to be fixed for a new installation is the height above ground of the telescope datum point, that is, the intersection of polar and declination axes. It is well known from many site surveys that micro-fluctuations of air temperature, evident near the ground, decrease with height above it and that seeing improves as a result. The difficulty lies in striking a balance between seeing and the cost of the building and dome, for of the total cost mentioned earlier, about M£1·25 will be absorbed by these items, even if the height of the telescope datum is kept down to 20 m or so. This dimension tends to be an acceptable compromise for the new generation of very large instruments. There is thus considerable headroom within the building below the observing floor and into this space are built several additional floors, one or possibly two of which serve the telescope directly as we shall see, the remainder being used for less direct functions, such as library, offices, administration, stores, and maintenance facilities. The main frame of the telescope penetrates the observing floor and is mounted at the top of a massive concrete pier which rises from its ground foundation, right through the building, passing without physical contact through a hole in each floor. This obviates any vibration in the building being transmitted to the telescope.

Topping the static building is a circular rail track upon which the dome rotates, computer controlled and power driven. The purpose of the dome is to afford weather protection to the observing floor equipment and to reduce the heating effect of the Sun during the day, for it is common practice to maintain the daytime temperature within the dome at the level forecast for the ensuing night to obviate serious convection currents across the line of sight when the dome shutters are opened for observing. It is thus double skinned, externally heat reflective and may be interlined with thermally insulating material or supplied with cooled air circulating between the skins.

The opening in the dome through which the telescope has access to the sky, is closed when not in use, by one of two basic forms of shutter. In either case the opening is about twice as wide as the telescope aperture, which relaxes the accuracy required of the drive. Shutter (a) is the up-and-over type, a rather complex form of which is shown at fig. 6.14. Here it is divided into four separately powered sections which are automatically manipulated to expose minimum opening. This arrangement provides the telescope with maximum protection from the force of the wind. In the form of a one-piece shutter it can only be driven to expose progressively from horizon to zenith, in which case windscreens inside the opening are deployed to provide similar protection. Shutter (b) is the bi-parting type, which exposes the whole opening every time sky access is required by small sideways movements in opposite directions of each half of the shutter. The larger of the two domes at Pic-du-Midi, fig. 8.1, is shown with such a shutter in the open position. Internal windscreens are essential. The up-and-over type is the less simple to seal against the weather but has the advantage of offering little resistance to wind. The bi-parting shutter in the open condition can apply considerable torque to the dome due to asymmetrical wind resistance and a higher power dome drive is required to accommodate the extra load.

A further function of the dome is to perform as the load-bearing structure for one or more permanent cranes, perhaps up to 25 tonnes capacity, which serve both as original installation equipment and to

155

facilitate any major overhaul work which may arise during the life of the telescope which will certainly exceed 50 years.

Mention was made in Chapter 5 of the need for a quick change of upper ends of some telescopes and this also requires specialized dome equipment. Either of two methods is generally used. One is to slew the telescope to the zenith position and to engage the top end with semi-automatic power driven fitments attached to one of the permanent cranes. The detached top end is then conveyed to an assigned storage fixture within the dome. The new top end is picked up from the storage fixture and fitted to the telescope as a reversal of the removal procedure. It is a fairly quick method, taking about 30 minutes to complete, but it is not favoured by some designers who decline the presumed risk of dangling heavy and expensive equipment upon crane ropes in the dark. The second method is to slew the telescope to the north horizontal position (in northern hemisphere sites) in which attitude it is in alignment with a floor-mounted transfer machine, power-driven to remove the top end and then to convey it to a nearby storage fixture where the new unit is selected, conveyed and fitted to the telescope. While the tube is horizontal, special retaining devices engage the edge of the primary mirror to prevent it from falling from its cell. Twenty minutes is claimed as the time required for the operation and with either method correct collimation is achieved by permanent locators at the interface of the upper Serrurier ring and the alternative upper ends.

To improve temperature stability inside the dome, the large installation is provided with a thick, water cooled concrete observing floor with a high heat storage capacity which forms (to use the engineer's expression) a ' thermal flywheel ' with all the stability which that implies. The water cooling is activated mostly during the daytime when the tendency is for the temperature to rise.

Into the dome too, from lower levels, comes the mass of piped and wired services required to support a large telescope and associated equipment. To list them all serves little purpose but one will recall the size of the problem in respect of computer control wiring alone, from Chapter 6. Pressurized oil for the hydrostatic bearings is of course a vital piped service, water is required for various cooling functions and vacuum service provides the suction for retaining the secondary mirror and for clamping photographic plates in their holders ; especially useful if the field is curved, for the plate is then forced to the curvature of the perforated holder. With the increasing use of photoelectric detectors cooled to cryogenic temperature for work in the infrared, even the supply of liquefied gas has joined the network and the resultant pipe and wiring looms are tending to overburden the telescope with festoons of services. This situation will improve with the recent development of the ' multiplexer ', a composite umbilical cord, embracing a comprehensive spread of mixed services in a single, flexible sheath.

Of all the routine maintenance functions, re-aluminizing the primary mirror requires the heaviest and most costly equipment. It is carried out at one- to two-yearly intervals, depending upon the site and requires the mirror and its cell to be removed from the telescope. Removal and refitting are performed with the telescope in the stowed (zenith) position. The usual arrangement is for a hydraulic elevating platform to be installed immediately below, and in alignment with the stowed telescope tube, such that the platform may be raised through a hole in the observing floor. The Cassegrain cage is stripped from the telescope and the platform is raised to engaged the back of the exposed cell which is then released from the lower Serrurier truss. The platform carrying the mirror in its cell then descends through the observing floor to the next floor down, where the mirror is transferred to the vacuum aluminizing chamber (see Chapter 4) which is installed there for the purpose. Whether the mirror is removed from its cell for treatment depends upon the design of the mirror suspension, or on the priority given to the economy of a smaller chamber for the mirror alone or to the reduction in down-time of the telescope gained by a chamber large enough to receive the whole cell. In this last case, everything but the mirror surface is masked off. The rectangular hole in the observing floor below the telescope may be seen behind the temporary staging in fig. 9.9, which shows the 158 inch telescope of Kitt Peak in an advanced stage of construction.

The aluminizing equipment is also used of course, to service the secondary mirrors which do not present such handling problems because of their smaller size and weight, and the coudé flats which are usually serviced in sets. During the period between aluminizing the mirrors are washed at intervals of 3 to 6 months, the primary mirror usually being treated in the telescope driven to the horizontal position. Ingress of water-based cleansing fluid into the cell is prevented by liberal application of sealing tape to all possible places of entry.

The diagram fig. 8.3 shows the diversity of equipment one floor below the 1·2 m telescope of the Dominion Astrophysical Observatory, Victoria, B.C. It is interesting to compare the horizontal coudé spectrograph with the inclined instrument of the 98 inch Isaac Newton shown in fig. 7.4 (a) page 138. Starlight from the 1·2 m telescope (fig. 5.4) is folded through 90° by the turret (fig. 5.6) in the slit room, to horizontal alignment with the spectrograph. In the typical large

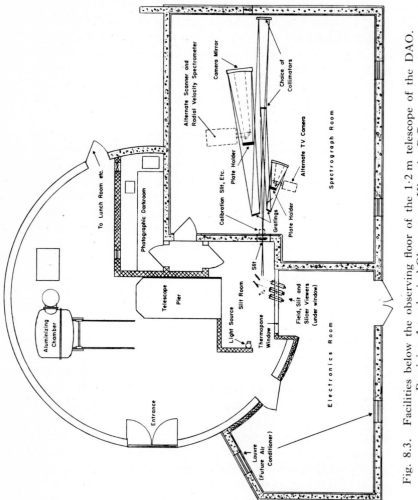

Fig. 8.3. Facilities below the observing floor of the 1·2 m telescope of the DAO. *Dominion Astrophysical Observatory, Victoria, B.C.*

modern observatory all the close support equipment for the telescope, comprising computers, darkroom and laboratories are to be found on the two levels immediately below the observing floor.

The highly specialized purpose of an observatory calls for some equally specialized requirements and just one, which is rather unexpected, is to provide red light illumination to all the facilities within the building, which may be visited by an observer during the working night. Subdued red light only minutely bleaches the visual purple in a person's dark-adapted eye (see Chapter 4) whereas even short exposure to bright white light would reduce retinal sensitivity for many minutes.

In remote locations currently favoured, it is sometimes difficult to bring national utility services to the site and the observatory will require to produce its own power. Diesel generating capacity up to 400 or 500 kVA and standby equipment are not uncommon at a large installation. Such machinery, together with engineering workshop, water pumps, air compressors, vacuum pump and pumped oil supply to the hydrostatic telescope bearings, are all potential sources of unwelcome vibration and it is customary to plan for these services to be housed in buildings separate from the main structure and to insert vibration damping devices between the machinery and its foundations to block any disturbance that might be transmitted through the ground to the telescope pier.

The supply of liquefied gases for cryogenic cooling of photoelectric sensors presents something of a problem, but on the latest assessment it is thought that if there are three or more telescopes at work at one observatory site, it is best, from the viewpoint of both cost and convenience, to lay down gas liquefaction plant at the site. For the demands of one or two instruments, transport of the liquid gases in Dewar flasks from the nearest supply point is more sensible although not, perhaps, so convenient, and far more gas is lost in evaporation during transportation and subsequent storage.

CHAPTER 9

some large telescopes

In this chapter ten modern telescopes are reviewed. Four are in service and the remainder are either being built or awaiting installation at the time of writing. It is hoped that the latter will be producing data before the end of this decade; certainly they are planned to do so.

9.1. *The* 200 *inch telescope of the Palomar Observatory, U.S.A.*

The largest telescope in service in the world, the 200 inch is unique for many features other than its size. The idea for such a telescope arose in 1928 but the first astronomical photographs were not to be taken with it until 1949. The chosen aperture ratio of $f/3\cdot3$ resulted in a much shorter tube than would have been possible with the traditional reflector ratio of about $f/5$ of the large telescopes which preceded it. The mirror is worked from a cast Pyrex blank and although the mass is reduced using an intricate pattern of ribs on the back, the finished mirror weighs $13\cdot15$ tonnes. Reducing the mass of the mirror has two important consequences. First, the telescope as a whole is lighter by about *four times* the mass of removed glass because the required rigidity is obtained from a less massive structure. Secondly, less time is required for the mirror to reach thermal equilibrium following a change in ambient temperature.

The Serrurier truss, which now finds universal application in the design of large telescopes, was originally designed for the 200 inch telescope tube. This was also the first instrument of sufficient size to permit an observing cage at the prime focus. The cage is constructed in two sections, the lower of which houses many optical components, including the Cassegrain and coudé secondary mirrors which are swung aside when the prime focus is being worked. This allows the ray path from the primary mirror to converge at the plane of the prime focus, 30 inches above the prime focus observing floor in the manned upper section of the cage where the majority of photographic work is done. Figure 9.1 is a sectional drawing of the telescope and dome showing this detail.

Three hyperboloid secondary mirrors are held permanently available in the prime focus cage, one providing a Cassegrain ratio of $f/16$, the

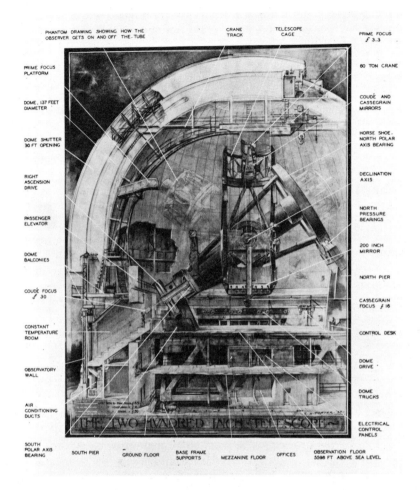

CRANE
TRACK

TELESCOPE
CAGE

PRIME FOCUS
ƒ 3.3

PRIME FOCUS
PLATFORM

80 TON CRANE

DOME, 137 FEET
DIAMETER

COUDÉ AND
CASSEGRAIN
MIRRORS

DOME SHUTTER
30 FT OPENING

HORSE SHOE.
NORTH POLAR
AXIS BEARING

RIGHT
ASCENSION
DRIVE

DECLINATION
AXIS

PASSENGER
ELEVATOR

NORTH
PRESSURE
BEARINGS

DOME
BALCONIES

200 INCH
MIRROR

NORTH PIER

COUDÉ FOCUS
ƒ 30

CASSEGRAIN
FOCUS ƒ 16

CONSTANT
TEMPERATURE
ROOM

CONTROL DESK

OBSERVATORY
WALL

DOME
DRIVE

DOME
TRUCKS

AIR
CONDITIONING
DUCTS

ELECTRICAL
CONTROL
PANELS

SOUTH
POLAR AXIS
BEARING

SOUTH PIER   GROUND FLOOR   BASE FRAME
SUPPORTS   MEZZANINE FLOOR   OFFICES   OBSERVATION FLOOR
5598 FT ABOVE SEA LEVEL

Fig. 9.1. The 200 inch telescope of Palomar. *The Mount Wilson and Palomar*
Observatories.

other two producing a coudé ratio of ƒ/30. One of these coudé-mirrors
is used on stars south of declination + 43°, in which case a single flat,
located at the intersection of declination and polar axes and driven at
half declination tube speed, directs the coudé beam from the secondary,
through the tubular polar axis to the coudé focus. For stars north of
declination + 43°, a further two flats direct starlight from the secondary,
past the edge of the primary (which in this declination range obstructs
the original ray path) and on, down through the polar axis as before.

M

These two ray paths are of different length and thus require secondary mirrors of different characteristics to produce a common equivalent ratio of $f/30$ for both coudé systems.

Another important innovation was the first application of hydrostatic bearings to the polar axis of a large telescope. Drives to polar and declination axes are both by worm and wheel, two drives being applied to the polar axis, one bearing the heavy loads of slewing, the other retaining its precision for setting and guiding.

9.2. *The 98 inch Isaac Newton telescope of the Royal Greenwich Observatory, Herstmonceux*

The 98 inch is the second largest telescope in service in Europe, surpassed only by the 102 inch telescope of the Crimea Astrophysical Observatory which was completed in 1961. The Isaac Newton Telescope was ordered in 1959 and saw first light in 1965. The unique feature (apart from its European status) is the polar disc equatorial mounting, dealt with in Chapter 4. This mounting is more suited to installation at high terrestrial latitudes than nearer to the equator because in the latter case the upper edge of the disc tends to obstruct access to objects low on the horizon opposite to the pole (north or south depending upon hemisphere). It is thus eminently suitable for the Herstmonceux site at latitude 50° 52′ N. The design, nevertheless, has been developed into the hybrid style characterized by some of the 3·5 to 4 m instruments, now in progress for installation at sites mainly less than 35° latitude. Some illustrations in this chapter show that the disc has been cut away to form a horseshoe. In some cases the fork blades remain on the upper face and in all cases mechanical stability is recovered by the provision of a polar shaft or its equivalent, projecting from the lower face and provided with a tail bearing.

Figure 9.2 shows the Isaac Newton telescope. Part of the observing floor is attached to the polar disc and so rotates through the same hour angle as the telescope. The bulbous housing at the eastern end (nearest the camera) of the declination axis contains the second coudé flat, the reflected beam passing through the hole seen in the fork blade immediately below the housing, on its way to the third coudé flat located below the disc and on the polar axis. The housing appears to be disproportionally large due to the perspective effects of close-up wide angle photography within the confines of the dome. The declination drive is at the west end of the axis and hence all but out of sight. From the photograph, note the difference in diameter of the tubes for the upper and lower Serrurier trusses (see Chapter 4), the Cassegrain chair its trackway and drive, (to keep it acceptably level while the telescope

Fig. 9.2. The 98 inch Isaac Newton Telescope. *RGO, Herstmonceux.*

is in drive) the observer, who shows the scale of the instrument, and the complex of piped and wired services.

9.3. *The* 60 *inch infrared flux collector of Tenerife*

Designed at Imperial College, University of London, the instrument is specifically designed to function in the infrared and through to the sub-millimetre wavelengths. Since 1972 the telescope has been used by the astronomy groups of several British universities at an altitude of 2350 m on the island of Tenerife, some 1000 to 1300 m above a strong atmospheric inversion layer which traps most of the cloud and precipitable water vapour below it, giving the optimum conditions for infrared astronomy.

The angular size of the sensitive patch of an infrared detector cell is typically about 8 arc seconds measured from the primary mirror and there is thus no purpose in striving for a star image of optical quality. This relaxation of performance specification results in the economy implicit in the schematic diagram of the tube at fig. 9.3. The primary concave ellipsoid 1, is only 127 mm thick, light in weight and fairly flexible. It is axially supported by an array of pre-loaded leaf springs

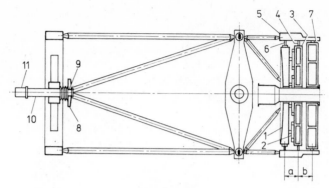

Fig. 9.3. The 60 inch infrared flux collector, Tenerife. *Imperial College, University of London.*

2, mounted upon the fabricated steel frame 3, which in turn is suspended by the flexible pin-beams 4, from the cell columns 5. These are coupled to the apices of the lower Serrurier truss. The mirror is radially supported by the flexible links 6, cemented to its periphery and made fast to the top of the columns 5. Item 7 is an aluminium fabricated frame to which the lower end of the members 5 are flexibly attached. The thermal expansivities of members 1 (glass), 3 (steel) and 7 (aluminium) relative to the distances *a* and *b* are such that a temperature change causes no significant strain in the mirror. The secondary mirror 8, a convex spheroid, is mounted upon a steel shaft 9, passing through a hole in its centre and coupled to a focusing screw inside the housing 10. The screw is driven by the motor 11, and provides sufficient axial focusing displacement of the single mirror to serve both Cassegrain and coudé functions.

The diagram does not pretend to show accurately all the details of this telescope tube, but sufficient may be seen to explain why it has been installed for an investment of about 10 per cent of that estimated for an optical instrument of similar aperture designed for photography in the blue and shorter wavelengths.

9.4. *The* 2·2 m *telescopes of the Max Planck Institut für Astronomie, Germany*

The 2·2 m telescopes of MPIA are two similar instruments, destined for a northern and a southern hemisphere site respectively, selected as explained in Chapter 8. Aperture ratios are prime focus $f/3$, Cassegrain $f/8$, coudé $f/40$ and the optical system conforms to the strict Ritchey-Chrétien solution. Coudé beam length is about 20 m, almost entirely contained within the dome, which is provided with air-conditioned atmosphere and water-cooled observing floor to improve internal seeing.

The line drawing of fig. 9.4 shows the unique four mirror coudé ray path (primary, secondary and two flats). The first flat reflects the beam from the secondary, not through a declination trunnion as is more usual, but away from the fork in a line coaxial with the polar axis, to incidence upon the externally mounted second flat seen high in the left hand side of the dome from whence it is reflected vertically through the observing floor to the coudé laboratory beneath. The arrangement requires special treatment of the tube centre section which, as the diagram shows

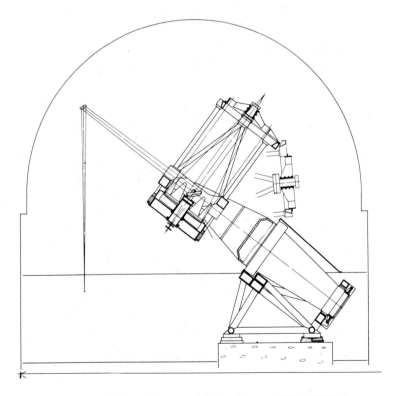

Fig. 9.4.   The 2·2 m telescope of Calar Alto.   *MPIA, Heidelberg.*

is ' twisted '. With the telescope set to zero declination (the equator) as shown, the coudé beam passes *above* the centre section and the path will be clear during telescope drive towards the north celestial pole (presuming we are in the northern hemisphere), until the upper end obscures the second flat.   To gain access to the southern sky, the tube is driven in declination to the north celestial pole after which the fork is rotated through 12 hours H.A.   The tube is then restored to the celestial equator, the coudé beam passing *below* the centre section to remain unobstructed while the southern sky is observed.

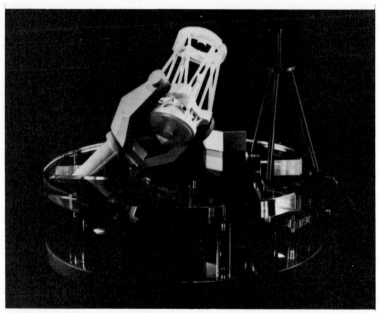

Fig. 9.5.   2·2 m telescope and coudé laboratory (model) *MPIA, Heidelberg.*

The photograph in fig. 9.5 is that of a model which gives an excellent impression of the complete installed telescope, the observing floor with pylon-mounted second flat (the pylon will eventually be replaced by an alternative mirror anchorage) and the coudé laboratory on the floor below.   Some engineering details are also unusual, for in addition to hydrostatic polar axis bearings, these telescopes are among the first equatorials to be designed with oil-pad declination bearings.   Once installed, polar axis bearings are subjected to *constant* proportions of radial and axial (journal and thrust) load, but the declination axis bearings suffer the complexity of these load vectors *changing sinusoidally with hour angle.*   Collection of the oil for recirculation (see Chapter 5)

166

was also a problem which has been effectively solved. The northern telescope will start work early in 1976; the southern is built, but awaits political approval of its site.

9.5. The 100 *inch telescope of Las Campanas Observatory, Chile*

Site selection for this telescope was dealt with in Chapter 8. It is possible that Las Campanas, presently administered by the Carnegie Institution, U.S.A., will eventually join Mount Wilson, Palomar and the Big Bear Solar Observatory, California, to form a four-site association under control of the governing body, Hale Observatories, U.S.A.

The 100 inch Irénée du Pont telescope, now under construction, is expected to go into service towards the end of 1975. It is to be a fork mounted instrument with a prime focus ratio of $f/3$ although no facility is provided at this position. The upper end embodies a permanent flip-cage carrying two secondary mirrors providing ratios of $f/7.3$ and $f/30$ for Cassegrain and coudé stations respectively. In addition, a plug-in secondary mirror offering $f/13$ Cassegrain facility for work in the infrared is provided and the unique feature of this is a mirror oscillating mechanism which displaces the star image on the photometer aperture through an amplitude of about 10 arc seconds at a frequency of 15 to 20 Hz. This action produces the image-chopping necessary for very faint star and infrared photometry (see Chapter 7).

Coudé arrangements are also a little unusual. For stars between $-20°$ declination and the south celestial pole, three mirrors only are employed. Light reflected from the flat is directed to the south, that is, away from the fork to a coudé spectrograph just *above* the observing floor. For stars north of $-40°$ declination, the three mirror system directs starlight down through the polar axis to a spectrograph in the more usual position below the observing floor. Thus, only three reflection losses are suffered, but computer control of the drive to the flat (which is independent of the telescope) is essential. Note that there is a declination overlap of 20° in which sky belt, either system may be used. A single element quartz corrector lens placed a little inside the Cassegrain focus produces a field 1·5 degrees square. This exceptional width can be obtained only upon a curved focal surface and the photographic plates are controlled to the right curvature by vacuum clamping the plate to a curved plateholder. Plates are typically of glass 1 mm thick and are sufficiently flexible for this treatment.

9.6. The 3·5 m *telescope of the Osservatorio Astronomico Nazionale, Italy*

Originating from an idea in the early 1960's, the design of this telescope began at the end of 1969. It was designed for installation between latitude 37° to 40° north, but it is possible that a site near Castelgrande in the Provincia de Potenza, at a latitude of 40°–49′ will be chosen when the project is restarted from its present state of abeyance. The instrument is to be fitted with an $f/4$ classical parabolic primary mirror and in this respect tends to revert to earlier optical specification. Two detachable upper ends will be used, one carrying prime focus equipment and an observer's cage, the other bearing the secondary mirrors for Cassegrain focus at $f/12$ and for coudé focus at $f/31\cdot3$. The upper ends are changed by the horizontal transfer method described in Chapter 8.

The photograph of fig. 9.6 shows a model of the telescope and the gracefulness attending $f/4$ geometry is immediately apparent in the long, slender upper Serrurier truss. The design of the basic fork mounting and the polar axis bearings is worthy of special notice. The blades of the fork are so designed that the very small deflection arising from their own structure weight and that of the tube is constant for all hour angles. The fork is a continuation of the polar shaft which takes the form of a large conical fabrication. The arrangement is convenient for directing the coudé beam, light being reflected from the first coudé flat (not present in the model), through the west declination trunnion to the second flat mounted within the elbow seen outboard of the declination bearing. From here the coudé beam is reflected down through the hollow western fork blade and polar cone to emerge from the coaxial hole in the south polar bearing, to incidence upon the third flat below the observing floor. This final mirror folds the beam to the requirement of a horizontal coudé spectrograph. Note also the declination drive at the western trunnion, the three point suspension of the mainframe upon the pier, and the model man in the foreground which gives scale to the whole instrument.

The north polar bearing is a thin slice of a sphere which interacts with two hydrostatic oil-pads, one of which is seen. The axes of the oil-pads converge to the polar axis and lie upon a common vertical plane. The point of intersection of the oil-pad axes, the centre of curvature of the sphere and the mass centre of the movable structure are coincident, which results in minimal net axial thrust and virtually no net moment about the north oil-pads. The south bearing is thus very lightly loaded and permits the application of a gimballed rolling element bearing, the small frictional drag arising, said to be helpful in damping externally excited vibration. Unlike the horseshoe mounting which (by definition) carries the penalty of a discontinuity in the great raceway, the Italian telescope may be driven through 24 hours continuous H.A. This is an advantage for tracking circumpolar stars and is consistent with modern thinking on daytime infrared astronomy.

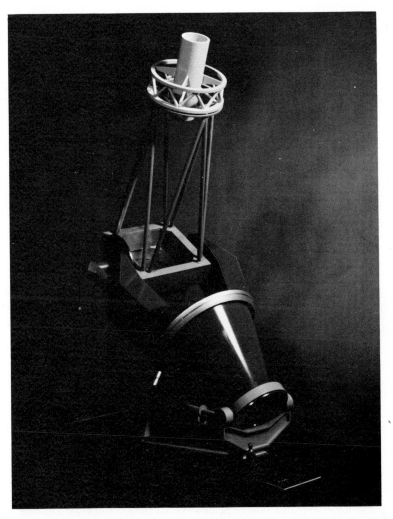

Fig. 9.6.   The 3·5 m telescope of the Osservatorio Astronomico Nazionale, Italy (Model). *Dilworth, Secord, Meagher & Associates.*

9.7. *The* 3·6 m *telescope of the European Southern Observatory*

Many references have been made to this telescope in the preceding chapters, dealing with specific aspects of design and construction, and it only remains to sum up briefly.   The initial studies for such a telescope were carried out as early as 1953 (nine years before the ESO consortium was formed), the great fused-quartz mirror blank was ordered in 1965, and operation at an altitude of 2240 m on Cerro La Silla, Chile will commence during 1976 at the earliest.

The chosen optical geometry is quasi-Ritchey-Chrétien, a small departure from the strict R-Ch form which allows optimization of the telescope as a whole by providing a dioptric corrector for astigmatism and field curvature. Three interchangeable upper ends are provided, one each for prime focus work at $f/3$, a Cassegrain secondary mirror of $f/8$ and a coudé secondary of $f/30$. A long focus coudé secondary of $f/150$ is also planned, and it is hoped to include this small element in the Cassegrain upper end. The diagram of fig. 9.7 shows the position of

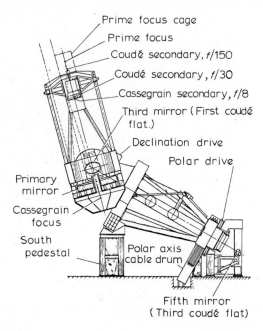

Fig. 9.7. The 3·6 m telescope of ESO, La Silla. *ESO, TP Division*, Geneva.

these mirrors and of the prime and Cassegrain foci. Also shown is the depth of the immensely rigid centre section which leaves too little space to suspend the mirror cell on a Serrurier truss. Six flexion bars are employed to replace it.

The mounting is a hybrid of fork and horseshoe styles, the development of which is described under the 98 inch Isaac Newton heading earlier in this chapter. As with all other telescopes of this size, the polar axis is on oil-pad bearings ; but to date it is probably the largest equatorial to be fitted with hydrostatic bearings at the declination axis as well. Note also in fig. 9.7, the cable wrap around the north polar bearing (take care, for this is a southern hemisphere telescope) bringing essential services to the instrument.

9.8. *The 3·9 m Anglo-Australian telescope of Siding Spring, Australia*

In 1967 the governments of Australia and the United Kingdom, agreed to fund this southern hemisphere telescope, south and east elevations of which are shown in fig. 9.8. The design follows fairly

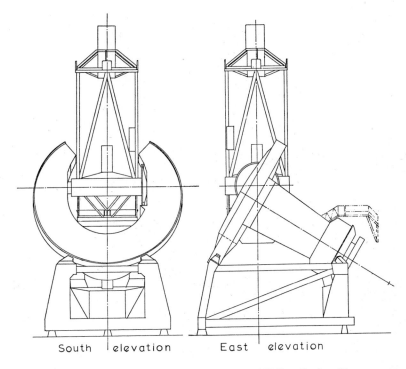

Fig. 9.8. The 3·9 m Anglo-Australian telescope of Siding Spring Observatory. *AAT Board, Canberra and ESO, Geneva.*

closely that of the 158 inch AURA telescopes, one of the few differences being that the declination axis is offset 107 cm above the polar axis to improve the uniformity of section modulus around the horseshoe. Comparison of the horseshoes of figs. 9.8 and 9.9 illustrates the improvement, but an additional mass in the form of a counterweight is needed to restore balance. Five damped hydrostatic bearings are applied to the

171

polar axis ; and separate journal and thrust roller bearings applied to the declination axis are elaborately mounted to ensure perfect squareness between the two axes, and to equalize other deflection forces.

Ritchey-Chrétien optics are employed, the primary mirror receiving air pad (axial) and lever (radial) support. The secondary mirrors and coudé flats have vacuum (axial) and mercury band (radial) support. Deflection problems of the upper Serrurier truss have required that the equipment needs at the prime focus shall be distributed between three interchangeable upper ends. One bears the prime focus instruments and the observing cage, one an $f/8$ Cassegrain secondary mirror and the third an $f/15$ Cassegrain and an $f/36$ coudé secondary mirror, selectable on powered mountings. The top ends are all powered by a common focusing motor permanently attached to the upper Serrurier ring and are changed by the overhead method described in Chapter 8.

This telescope will operate under a computer control which is as advanced and comprehensive as that of any of the large instruments in progress. Installed at Siding Spring at an altitude of 1300 m, the telescope datum point is at the great height of 29·5 m above the ground in a concrete building surmounted by a steel dome. It is expected to be fully operational on the first day of 1975.

9.9 *The* 158 *inch telescopes of AURA, U.S.A.*

Very early in the 1960's, the Associated Universities for Research in Astronomy started work on a project for a 150 inch telescope which was eventually to be installed at Kitt Peak, Arizona and in 1967 a similar telescope was added to the programme for installation at Cerro Tololo, Chile. Both are fitted with Ritchey-Chrétien optics and all the mirrors are made of Cervit except for the primary of the KPNO telescope which is of fused quartz and which, while designed for a 150 inch telescope, turned out to be 158 inches (4 m) in diameter. The KPNO instrument was dedicated in June 1973, and observation commenced in August 1974. Limited operation of the CTIO telescope is expected by early 1976. During the development of these great short-focus telescopes (the KPNO instrument has a prime focus ratio of $f/2·6$ due to the unexpectedly large primary mirror) there has grown an opinion that the prime focus facility is less productive than the Cassegrain, because the sum of the losses at the secondary mirror and at the relatively simple Cassegrain corrector are lower than the losses through a complex prime focus corrector. The Cassegrain ratios, typically $f/8$ are also more suited to spectroscopy, and on telescopes of this size, powerful spectrographs may be mounted conveniently.

Figure 9.9 is a photograph of the KPNO (northern hemisphere)

Fig. 9.9. 158 inch telescope of Kitt Peak. *KPNO, Arizona.*

instrument in an advanced stage of erection. The great north horseshoe resting upon two hydrostatic bearing pads dominates the picture. The telescope is pointing south at a substantial minus declination angle and to about 4 hours H.A. The back of the mirror cell is seen within the Cassegrain cage and the rectangular holes in the horseshoe offer access to the declination bearings and second coudé flat. The mesh panels enclosing the Cassegrain cage serve an important protective function for on a telescope of this size, depressed to low elevation, the observer will find himself 6 or 7 metres above the observing floor and in the dark !

The seeing at CTIO is better than at KPNO but the ground is not quite so stable in Chile and the relevant building, dome and contents are accordingly designed to withstand horizontal seismic shock up to $0 \cdot 3\ g$.

9.10 *The* 6 m *telescope of the Academy of Sciences of the U.S.S.R.*

In 1960 the government of the U.S.S.R. authorized the construction of this telescope and extensive surveys finally fixed a site at an altitude of 2070 m on Mount Semirodniki on the northern slopes of the Caucasian chain.   Work on the building started in 1966 and it was expected that the telescope would go into service in late 1972.   This immense telescope is predictably attended by immense problems, some of which, it seems, await solution at the time of writing.   It is by far the largest telescope in the world, surpassing the 200 inch of Palomar in primary mirror area, by some 40 per cent.   One hopes that first light will not be too long delayed.

The primary aperture ratio at $f/4$ is high for a modern telescope, and gives a focal length of 24 m.   There is no provision for either Cassegrain or Coudé stations, but referring to the line diagram fig. 9.10 (*a*), the permanent upper end carries a prime focus observing cage 1,

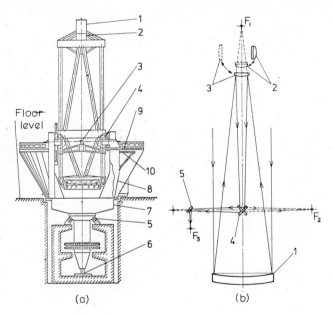

Fig. 9.10.   The 6 m telescope of the Academy of Sciences of the USSR.
(a) General arrangement.   (b) Optical layout.

174

beneath which is suspended a cell 2, containing a two-element prime focus correcting lens and an $f/31$ secondary mirror which gives an equivalent focal length of 186 m at the Nasmyth focus. Each optical component is power-retracted when the other is in use. Light from the secondary is reflected by the diagonal flat 3, out of the tube through an elevation trunnion 4, to the Nasmyth focus. The primary mirror is of borosilicate glass (Pyrex type) and is ground spherical on the back to give approximately constant thickness for improved thermal reaction. The telescope is carried upon an altazimuth mounting. Six hydrostatic oil pads 5, and a steady bearing 6, are provided for the azimuth axis and hydrostatic bearings are also applied to the elevation trunnions. The main platform 7, is level with the dome floor and from the platform rise the fork blades 8 which carry the elevation bearings at their tips. They also carry the observing deck 9, and the platform 10, upon which is mounted Nasmyth focus ancillary equipment as required. The fork blades are of sufficient size for one of them to contain a permanent para-coudé spectrograph with access facilities, the other containing a staircase, lift and services.

Figure 9.10 (b) is a schematic diagram of the ray path where 1 is the primary mirror, 2 the prime focus corrector (centred and retracted), 3 the secondary mirror (similarly deployed), 4 the Nasmyth diagonal flat, and 5 the para-coudé flat. F_1 is the prime focus and the flat 4, may be flipped to serve either the ancillaries at the Nasmyth focus F_2 on platform 10, fig. 9.10 (a) or the para-coudé spectrograph slit, F_3 via the flat 5, fig. 9.10 (b).

The altazimuth mount, almost essential to a telescope of this size and weight, is mechanically superior to the equatorials because among lesser advantages, vertical loading is constant and symmetrical, azimuth rotation causes no load changes or deflections and tube flexure is in one plane, dependent only upon zenith angle. Disadvantages are the complexity of the sidereal drive, an inaccessible sky area of about 5 degrees radius centred upon zenith, and a rotating field. The latter is corrected for photography by driving the plateholder in counter-rotation.

The ten telescopes reviewed have been carefully chosen for their unique features, yet all but the Russian (in a class by itself) add up to the most modern thinking in rationalized large telescope design. The six in progress (eight, if we include the duplication of the AURA and MPIA telescopes) do not exhaust the list, for there remain, among others, the French 3·6 m of INAG and the German 3·5 m of MPIA. There also exists a 157 inch diameter, fused silica mirror blank in the possession of the Canadian authorities which must eventually serve in a major telescope, but that is for the future.

CHAPTER 10
extra-terrestrial telescopes

EVIDENCE has been given in the preceding chapters to show the degrading effect of the atmosphere upon image quality, and the improvement to be gained at high altitude sites. There is an obvious limit to this improvement with the ground-based telescope, and reviewed in this chapter are four telescopes which have been freed from the limitation. Two are balloon lifts to stratospheric altitude and so leave most of the atmosphere beneath them, and two are telescopes in Earth orbit, above all but the most tenuous traces of gas.

10.1. *Stratoscope I*

Stratoscope I identifies a combination of balloon, parachute, telemetry equipment and telescope, produced to the requirement of Princeton University, U.S.A., which has the distinction of being the first unmanned telescope to leave the ground in the quest for better photographs. There is a very high cost incurred with each flight because near-perfect weather is required for a safe launch (with all the costly delays which that implies), one great helium filled balloon is lost at each flight, and substantial damage is suffered by the equipment at each parachute landing. The telescope, specially designed and built by Perkin-Elmer for solar photography is of Newtonian form and has a 30 cm × $f/8$ fused quartz primary mirror figured to the unprecedented accuracy of 0·1 of a wavelength, from which it achieved resolution very near to the diffraction limit of the aperture.

It was flown for the first time on 25 September 1957 from New Brighton, Minnesota and attained an altitude of 25 000 m, that is, above about 96 per cent of the atmosphere, at which height the instrument was pre-programmed to seek the Sun using onboard sensors and then to expose 8000 frames of 35 mm film at two-second intervals, each exposure lasting 0·0015 second. Because the performance was not monitored from the ground the programme included slow oscillation of a focusing mechanism which ensured that some of the exposures would be of the highest possible quality, though to the detriment of the majority. In the event, only ten frames turned out to be of the expected superb definition, but this was sufficient encouragement to develop a series of improvements to the servo guiding mechanism and mirror mounting, and also to add a television facility that enabled ground workers to monitor performance and to guide the telescope to specific details on the Sun's disc. At the conclusion of photography, the telescope was put to the stowed position by remote control and a small explosive charge was fired to cut the parachute from the balloon which, freed from the load leapt upwards to its destruction by the suddenly expanded gas, whilst the telescope descended to a hard parachute landing.

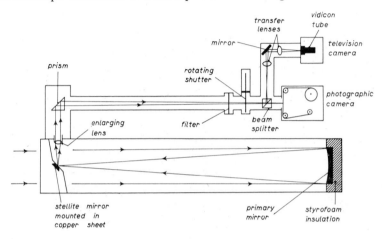

Fig. 10.1.   Schematic diagram of Stratoscope I optics.   *Perkin-Elmer Corporation.*

Figure 10.1 shows a diagram of the optical system embodied in the modified equipment. The primary mirror focuses a 23 mm diameter image of the Sun and within this image at the focal plane, is fixed a tiny (2 × 2 mm) diagonal flat mirror made from stellite, a hard metal alloy which retains most of its physical characteristics at high temperatures. The enlarging lens of × 25 power produces an equivalent focal ratio of $f/200$ at the plane of the film. A rotary shutter in front of the film governs the frequency and duration of the exposures and a prism beam splitter between shutter and film produces simultaneous, identical images upon the film and upon the vidicon tube of the television camera, the latter being required for the essential purpose of ground control. The success of the revised equipment is shown in fig. 10.2 which is a photograph of a sunspot and surrounding granulation taken from Stratoscope I at an altitude of 24 400 m on 17th August 1959. The ' granules ' seen are the heads of enormous convection currents of gas rising from the Sun's hot interior, and each measures between about 320

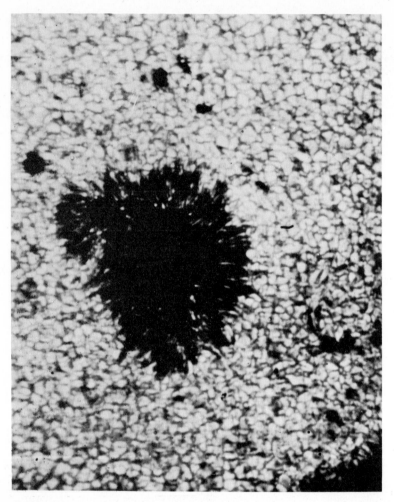

Fig. 10.2. Solar photograph from Stratoscope I, showing sunspots and granulation. *Perkin-Elmer Corporation.*

and 1600 km across. The definition is better than *any* solar photograph taken with *any* ground-based telescope before that date.

10.2. *Stratoscope II.*

The success of sending up a small telescope by balloon led Princeton University astronomers to develop a much larger and more sophisticated experiment called Stratoscope II. Intended for high definition night observation, the telescope was built like its predecessor by Perkin-

Elmer. It is a 91 cm × $f/4$ modified Gregorian reflector which, with its associated control and telemetry equipment weighs 3600 kg. Of the flights which began in the late 1960's, one took place during the night of 26th–27th March 1970 when the complex was launched from Palestine, Texas, on an 800 km voyage down wind. The ceiling was reached at 24 400 m in 110 minutes from launch and after a short period for adjustments (from the ground) and temperature stabilization, 9 hours of observing time ensued (that is, until daylight) during which some of the sharpest photographs ever taken of the planets Jupiter and Uranus, the Seyfert Galaxy NGC 4151 and the star Eta Virginis were obtained.

Stratoscope II carries no pre-programmed instructions and complete control of all aspects of a flight is carried out remotely from a ground station. This provides far more flexibility of observation, but it also demands a far higher level of complexity in the control system to optimize the images which come very near to the diffraction limit to resolving power of this quite large telescope.

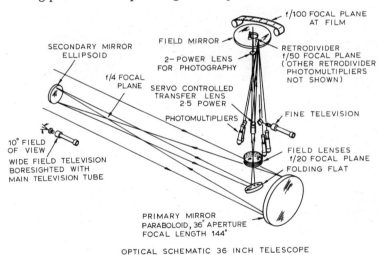

OPTICAL SCHEMATIC 36 INCH TELESCOPE

Fig. 10.3.   Schematic diagram of Stratoscope II optics. *Perkin-Elmer Corporation.*

Figure 10.3 is a diagram of the ray path through the telescope. Light from the secondary mirror is intercepted by a diagonal flat and is reflected out through the side of the tube to a photographic and guidance facility, optical details of which are shown. This geometry in effect folds the complete optical path of the instrument into a 90° vee-shaped structure which benefits mechanical balance as we shall see. At the end

179

of the side-arm so formed is a field mirror with a central hole, behind which is a 70 mm film camera. The star-field (50 arc minutes wide) reflected from the field mirror is intercepted by a small diagonal flat which re-directs it to focus upon the fine guiding television camera shown. Of interest is the tracking arrangement. Two retrodividers (shown dotted before the face of the field mirror) are capable of being

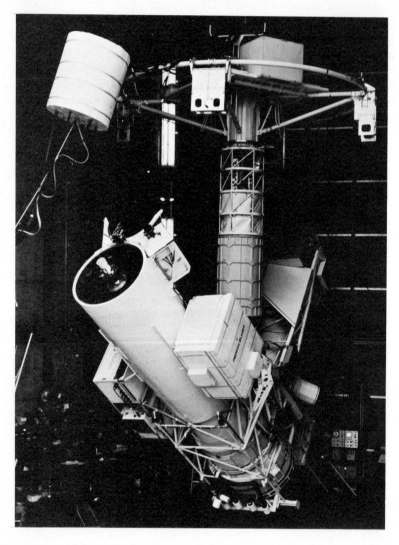

Fig. 10.4.   Stratoscope II telescope on a test rig in the maker's works.   *Perkin-Elmer Corporation.*

driven under ground control, to any position within the field boundary. These devices are in effect tiny reflecting pyramids, the faces of which are so designed that wherever they are in the field, if the image of a star (which is 24 μm diameter) falls centrally upon the apex of one of them, it is split into four separate beams of equal intensity, each being received by a photomultiplier. The slightest shift of the image from the retro-divider apex causes an imbalance of luminance between the four receptors which combine to produce a corrective signal for re-centring the star. Two sets of retrodividers and photomultipliers are present (only one set is shown), enabling the telescope to be locked onto two reference stars in the field, the image of the object star then being held on the optical axis. The wide field (10°) television camera provides a similar facility at the ground monitor to the small ' finder ' clamped parallel to the axis of many ground based telescopes.

Figure 10.4 is a photograph of the telescope in the deployed configuration upon a test rig. The inclined telescope tube is seen flanked by the command box to the right of it, the telemetry box to the left and the wide field television camera above the open tube end. The side-arm containing all the fine guiding equipment described above is seen standing off from the tube at 90° and to the rear of it. The vertical cylindrical structure is the azimuth frame beneath which the three orthogonal operating axes intersect at a point coincident with the mass centre of the tube and side-arm assembly. Because the telescope has a basic altazimuth mounting, the third axis is required to rotate the tube about an axis parallel to its own in order to keep station with the rotating field. Above the azimuth frame is the inertia wheel against which a servo motor reacts to drive the telescope in azimuth. The white drum (top left), normally above the telescope in flight, contains the antennae necessary for radio control.

Figure 10.5 shows the 195 m tall flight train soon after launch. The telescope hangs in the stowed configuration (tube vertical) just below the antennae. Next comes the emergency back-up parachute with canopy collapsed. The main balloon envelope, still in its shroud, follows and above this the helium-inflated pilot balloon provides the 7200 kg lift required at launch. At 3000 m the shroud is jettisoned and the gas in the pilot balloon is allowed to expand into the main envelope to a final volume of 141 000 m³. At the conclusion of observing, the telescope is returned to the stowed condition and the balloon is valved down to the ground without deployment of the parachute which is there as a safeguard against balloon failure. The balloon is expendable with each flight, and the telescope suffers damage to an extent depending on how and where it lands.

Fig. 10.5. Stratoscope II flight-train soon after launch. *Perkin-Elmer Corporation.*

10.3. *The ESRO ultraviolet telescope S2/68*

Astronomy from the stratosphere solves most of the problems of poor seeing but the thin air remaining above the telescope still forms an effective barrier to ultraviolet and shorter wavelength radiation, and to overcome this hindrance an increasing number of telescopes and other shortwave experiments have been rocketed into space. Such facilities comprise the payload of the European Space Research Organization (ESRO) spacecraft designated TD-1A, launched by an American Thor-Delta rocket, from the Western Test Range, California on 12th March 1972. The spacecraft was injected into a nearly circular orbit, the axis of which was aligned with the Sun and remains so due to a retrogressive rotation of the nodes upon the ecliptic plane (see saros cycle, Chapter 1) at the rate of 0·992° per day. Thus, for our immediate purpose, TD-1A orbits in continuous sunlight and control systems ensure that it is stabilized on three orthogonal axes, one of which (like that of the orbit), is also Sun-aligned. The spacecraft is rotated about this axis at orbital angular velocity (94·5 minutes period) and in the same direction, whereby its attitude is held constant relative to Earth.

The largest of the seven experiments on board is a 27·5 cm aperture × $f/3·5$ reflecting telescope designated S2/68, which was developed jointly by the Institute d'Astrophysique, University of Liège, Belgium and the Science Research Council, Great Britain. It is designed for spectroscopy in the bandwidth 133 nm to 263 nm and for photometry through the narrow range 260 nm to 300 nm. It has no independent guiding facility, and fixed within the TD-1A vehicle, is dependent upon the motion of latter for its sky coverage. The instrument is set within the spacecraft so that it points permanently in a direction away from the Earth and at 90° to the Earth/Sun line.

In the simplest terms, if one imagines the line between Earth and Sun to be an axle, the satellite orbit may be represented by the rim of a wheel mounted upon the axle at the Earth location. If the telescope is considered as fixed to the wheel rim so that the optical axis is radial to the wheel hub, that is the flight configuration of S2/68. Thus, every 94·5 minutes the telescope sweeps a complete, circular slice of the sky and hence covers the entire celestial sphere in 6 months because the 'axle' about which it is orbiting swings 180° about the Sun during that period. The experiments on board TD-1A are designed to take place in this environment of continuous sunlight but in fact orbital cyclic variations to the simple model described resulted in a satellite eclipse sequence (the satellite passing into Earth's shadow once during each orbit) occuring between November 1972 and February 1973, that is, following the planned 33 weeks life of the project. However, results were so good and demands upon on-board energy were so small that the satellite was put into hibernation mode on 29th October 1972 and was restored to action for a further unanticipated research programme in mid-February 1973.

Figure 10.6 is a cut-away diagram of the S2/68 telescope which shows the primary mirror tilted to focus the field centre upon the prime focus slit assembly in the box of spectrophotometric equipment that is secured to the side of the telescope tube. Because the instrument operates in continuous sunlight, concern was felt in the design stage that light scattering in the tube might impair performance but the light baffles shown have controlled this successfully.

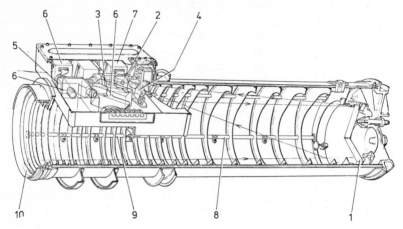

Fig. 10.6.   ESRO ultraviolet orbiting telescope S2/68.   1, Primary mirror. 2, Prime focus slit assembly.   3, Secondary mirror.   4, Plane diffraction grating.   5, Exit slits and Fabry housing.   6, Spectrophotometric detectors (photomultipliers).   7, Photometric detector (photomultiplier). 8, Lower baffle stack.   9, Upper baffle stack.   10, Sun baffle assembly. *Science Research Council, London.*

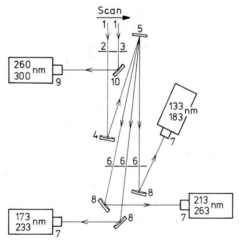

Fig. 10.7.   Layout of the spectrophotometric equipment on board the S2/68 orbiting telescope.

Figure 10.7 is a diagram of the ray paths within the equipment box. The rays 1 represent the central ray of a star image reflected from the primary mirror. It is shown in two positions because the motion of the spacecraft scans the image of the star across the spectrometer slit 2, and then across the photometer slit 3 located on the plane of prime focus. The secondary mirror 4 reflects light emerging from the slit 2 to the reflection grating 5, which disperses the beam to the exit slits 6 which are on the focal plane of the secondary mirror/grating combination. Three photomultipliers 7 are illuminated by their respective slits 6 via the Fabry imaging mirrors 8. The photomultipliers are marked with their dynamic wavelength range in nm. Undispersed light from the photometer slit 3 illuminates the photomultiplier 9, via the Fabry mirror 10.

10.4. *The NASA LST Project*

Ever since space flight became a reality, and until the late 1960's, it was every astronomer's wish to send a large manned telescope into orbit—or better still, to base one upon the airless surface of the Moon. More recent experience, resulting mainly from the Apollo series of manned Moon flights and the enormous thrust capacity of the great rockets available now and in the near future, has changed this outlook.

The National Aeronautics and Space Administration (NASA), U.S.A., has a forward project for putting into Earth orbit, in 1980, a telescope and associated equipment weighing between 9 and 11 tonne. The whole complex, named LST (Large Space Telescope) will have better resolving power than any telescope ever constructed by that date, because the airless environment of space makes possible the operation of a *diffraction limited telescope*, that is, one in which resolution depends *only* upon the primary mirror aperture, the accuracy of form and alignment of the optical components, and the wavelength of the signal. (see Chapter 3). In this respect it is planned to operate the instrument through the enormous spectral bandwidth from 100 nm to the far infrared. The LST is to be a 120 inch (3m) aperture instrument of $f/2\cdot2$ prime focal ratio, and $f/12$ Cassegrain focal ratio, conforming to the Ritchey-Chrétien solution. Diffraction-limited performance is attainable only if the wavefront is held perfect to within $0\cdot25\lambda$ and the aim is to figure the mirrors to $0\cdot05\lambda$ r.m.s., a small improvement upon the minimum requirement. Thus, within a field semi-angle of 5 arc minutes, resolution of $0\cdot04$ arc seconds (which is very near to the diffraction limit) will be attained. Image quality is still adequate for the necessary offset guide star function out to a field semi-angle of 24 arc minutes.

To attain this performance, pointing accuracy to within ± 1 arc second will be required and stability or ' jitter ' must not exceed the extremely low value of $\pm 0{\cdot}004$ arc second during the exposures of up to 10 hours which are necessary to record stars down to magnitude $+29$ (that is more than 100 times dimmer than the faintest object detected through the 200 inch telescope at Palomar). It is this requirement of extreme stability which excludes manned operation of the telescope, for in the critical ' free-fall ' conditions in space, the smallest applied force will have a significant effect. It is calculated that even the heartbeat of a man in physical contact with the telescope would cause its stability to be upset to beyond the acceptable limit of $\pm 0{\cdot}004$ arc seconds.

There is now also plenty of evidence to show that the surface of the Moon is no place for a large, diffraction-limited telescope ; for even

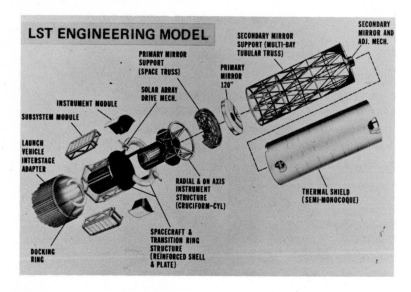

Fig. 10.8. Dissected model of the 120 inch orbiting telescope (LST) of NASA.
Boeing Aerospace Company.

disregarding the cost of establishing one there, the Apollo experimental programmes proved that the resonance of the Moon's crust and the seismic rumblings within combine to alter the earlier thoughts about its suitability. The advent of television and telemetry techniques in astronomy have diminished the need for an observer in space to the point where he can be just as effective sitting at a console in a comfortable ground-based laboratory.

It was the lift available from the Titan III rockets that first gave rise to thoughts of launching a telescope as large and massive as the LST. But this launch vehicle, essentially associated with the launch of a number of expendable telescopes over a ten year programme period, has now been abandoned in favour of the projected Space Shuttle, a winged cargo rocket which is planned to lift its first scheduled consignment, the LST, into circular orbit 611 km above ground and then return to its base for further service. The plan, to date, is to launch a single LST for a 15 year orbital life and to service it at intervals, using the Space Shuttle for the purpose. Service visits will take equipment and crew, skilled in both spaceflight and scientific instrument maintenance, to the LST for replacement of expendable on-board materials, inspection and adjust-

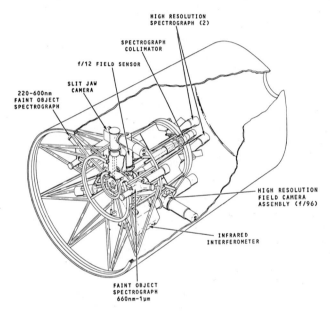

Fig. 10.9. Scientific instrument package of the LST. *NASA Marshall Spaceflight Center.*

ment, and to change failed, degraded or outdated components and equipment as the need arises. It is also possible to return the LST to Earth for refurbishing during the period if this appears to be necessary and then to restore it to orbit. The Space Shuttle will be used to return it to Earth at the end of the 15 year period in any case.

Figure 10.8 is a drawing of a dissected engineering model of the LST which shows that there is more complexity behind the primary mirror than there is in front of it. In fact, of the total cylindrical structure, 3·68 m diameter and 12·7 m long, a length of 5 m behind the mirror will be occupied by scientific instruments and support systems, for unlike a ground-based telescope which is served by slit room, coudé laboratory and all the other facilities of the observatory, the orbiting telescope has to carry its observatory upon its back, so to speak. Figure 10.9 shows the scientific instrument package in greater detail. Light from the telescope secondary mirror will enter the instrument package at the end nearest the reader, and will focus the field at the plane of the slit. This is viewed by a ground observer via the slit jaw camera shown, and a television monitor serving the same function as a slit viewer in a ground based slit room.

Project management of the LST has been assigned by NASA's Office of Space Science to its Marshall Spaceflight Centre, Alabama, and even now, Boeing Aerospace Company, Seattle has manufactured some of the more difficult engineering components and has constructed an LST test facility so adequately isolated from terrestrial interference, that is from seismic disturbance, temperature change, air movement and so on, that the stability of space is almost available here on the ground.

new developments

11.1. *Daytime use of the telescope*

UNTIL recently, daytime use of the telescope has been mainly confined to solar work, bright comets and the limited examination of some planets. Present day availability of infrared detectors, which are between them collectively sensitive to a wide range of infrared wavelengths, has greatly increased telescope potential and it is possible that round-the-clock work for large instruments may become normal in the future. Indeed, some telescopes are already on experimental daytime stellar work in addition to normal night observation. The 120 inch telescope of the Lick Observatory has been used extensively in this manner, and (to the relief of the observers involved), the quality of night seeing has been scarcely affected by this daytime activity. It appears that at Mount Hamilton there is a little more airborne dust about by day than by night (detectable only by particle count tests), but a small compensating increase in the frequency of mirror washing and 'house cleaning' is a small price to pay for the extra hours of daily observing time. There are some essential daytime precautions to be taken, like the avoidance of accidentally setting fire to the dome by focusing sunlight on its interior surface, and also the prevention of sunlight falling directly upon the observing floor through the dome slit because a warm floor is an intense radiator in the infrared.

Examination of a simplified model of the daytime sky will help in understanding the problems of infrared astronomy. Such a model presumes, for maximum luminance values, that all diffuse light scattering is downwards and that this produces maximum radiance from a bright cloud approximately equal to 2×10^{-5} of the Sun's radiance. Infrared *scattering* in a clear sky is about 10 per cent of this value and is composed mainly of wavelengths $< 4\mu$m to which must be added thermal *emission* of the air mass at wavelengths $> 4\mu$m. The intensity of these radiation components is shown by the respective curves on the graph of fig. 11.1, which together produce the total energy distribution for an idealized sky with minimum radiance at 4μm. Scattered energy disappears at sunset but emitted energy is permanent and poses big problems for observation beyond 5μm. But the black-body nature

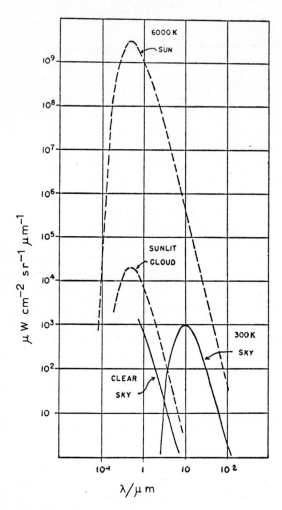

Fig. 11.1. Idealized spectral radiance curves for sky components. *University of Groningen and ESO, Geneva.*

presumed for this simplified model atmosphere, while being a useful introduction, is not entirely correct, for there are many infrared windows. Table 1 elaborates a little on the window details, the second column listing the bandwidth of the windows, the central wavelength of which is shown in the first column. The remaining columns are self-explanatory but it is interesting to note from column 3, how the radiation transition from scattering to emission takes place at about 4μm and from

λ μm	$\Delta\lambda$ μm	Radiation mechanism *	Absorption features λ μm	Absorber
			1·9	H_2O
2·2	0·4	S		
			2·7	H_2O
3·6	0·6	S+E		
			4·3	CO_2
5·0	0·5	E+S		
			6·3	H_2O
10·0	5·0	E	9·6	O_3
			15·0	CO_2
20·0	6·0	E	>17·0	H_2O

∗ S = Scattering, E = Emission

Table 1.   Infrared atmospheric windows.   *University of Groningen, and ESO, Geneva.*

column 5, how influential water vapour is in absorbing infrared energy over a very wide spectral range.   From Wien's displacement law it may be shown that the peak of the Planck distribution curve for black-body emission from air at 300 K is reached at a wavelength of about 10μm. This value is quite troublesome because since it is at about the middle of one of the ' windows ', when work is being done in this spectral region the emission shows up as noise at the detector.   But this and similar atmospheric thermal radiation effects are recognized and may be separated from the required signal by chopping the star image as described under photometry in Chapter 7.

The outcome of these phenomena and development of the means of dealing with them, is that daytime operation of the telescope in the infrared, particularly at 10μm and beyond, does not produce a result significantly inferior to night observation.   There is of course, the mechanical difficulty of centring the required star (which may well be quite invisible) on the photometer aperture or spectrograph slit, but this is done by offsetting as already explained in Chapter 7 for night photometry of very faint stars, since with a large telescope normally night-visible stars of magnitude +4 or 5 are visible in daylight.   Stars of this brightness tend towards the faintest which may be seen with naked eye on a clear night.   If no day-visible stars are in the field which includes the object of interest, centring the image can only be achieved by setting the telescope to known R.A. and declination co-ordinates ; but to do this the telescope must be of the highest order of mechanical accuracy with equally accurate computer control, and a pointing error of less than one arc second.

The daytime sky is about 3 magnitudes darker in the near infrared (at about $1\mu m$) than it is in the visible. At this order of wavelength, the image converter is brought to bear, with a corresponding increase in the number of faint infrared sources which may be seen. This technique has the further advantage that the output may be displayed upon a television monitor remote from the telescope.

The ability to detect and measure the signal from a star depends largely upon the strength of the standing signal against which the measurements are made and to appreciate the significance of this, one can imagine one's eye placed at the position of the detector. Everything within view, and at a temperature which produces radiation in the wavelength passband being worked, will produce a signal at the detector, and thus an output from it. Most of the unwanted incident energy will be the standing signals arising from the sky, as we have seen, and also from the optical and structural components of the telescope and associated equipment. These typically comprise a field lens, ground from material of appropriate transmission characteristics immediately in front of the detector, followed by a cooled diaphragm perhaps 10 arc seconds in diameter, followed in turn by the telescope mirrors. The star image is formed upon the detector patch through the diaphragm and is supplemented by a standing signal arising from the image of the primary mirror, the spider and the edge of the secondary mirror. The mirrors contribute little to the total signal from their own radiation because emissivity of the reflective surfaces is very low. The spider is a more powerful source, emission from which cannot be reduced by aluminizing or polishing because it is then liable to reflect infrared radiation from all kinds of objects in the entire dome ; not the least powerful of these radiators is the observer himself, with peak emission just short of $10\mu m$ —just right for maximum interference in the $10\mu m$ passband region.

The spider may be removed altogether if the object under examination is bright enough (in the infrared) to abandon the flux-collecting power of the main telescope in favour of the siderostat in conjunction with an off-axis paraboloid mirror. The basic ray path for such a scheme is shown in fig. 11.2 where (a) is the altazimuth mounted siderostat, (b) is the paraboloid mirror, and (c) is a flat, fixed mirror directing the collected radiation to focus at the entrance diaphragm or slit (d) of the receiving instrument. Some coma and oblique astigmatism arise from the reflected object being displaced from the axis of symmetry of the paraboloid mirror but this may be either righted by using an appropriate dioptric corrector, or tolerated in the long wavelengths of infrared (section 3 Chapter 9). Using the most modern liquid helium-cooled detectors, low noise amplifiers and effective chopping methods (among other aids), object signal levels as low as 10^{-6} to 10^{-7} times the standing sky signal may be detected. For example, using a 4μm wide filter centred on a wavelength of 10μm, and a 10 arc second aperture, the standing signal incident upon the detector from all sources is typically about 10^{-8} W and in these conditions, the minimum detectable object signal is, with similar approximation, 3 to 4×10^{-14} W.

In all infrared work, whether astronomical or in any other field of science, it is preferable that the elements in the optical train are reflecting, because transmission losses beyond the limits of the visible spectrum are quite unacceptable through conventional optical glasses (depending upon wavelength and the thickness of glass involved). But

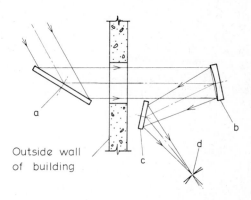

Fig. 11.2.   Ray path of an off-axis paraboloid mirror and siderostat.

lenses cannot always be avoided and for this and similar purposes a range of crystals have been developed, the optical characteristics of which allow selection of a material to suit most needs.   Many have very high refractive indices at extended wavelengths and thus suffer higher reflection losses than would glass (see Chapter 4).   Thallium bromo-iodide for example has a value for n of 2·22 at 4×10^4 nm, but the high transmittance obtained with these specialized crystals more than compensates for the reflection losses.   Indeed, for work in all but the shortest of the infrared wavelengths, their use is essential.   Absorption within a crystal is governed by interaction between the nature of the crystalline material and the flux propagated through it.   In the ultraviolet region absorption is due to a process involving the electronic energy states in the crystal whilst in the infrared the interaction is mainly between the electromagnetic photons and the lattice phonons (the vibrations of the array of atoms). The limits of useful transmission may be defined in an arbitrary manner, one accepted convention being to take the wavelengths at which total transmittance (that is taking into account reflection and absorption losses) falls to 10 per cent of the incident flux, through a crystal 2 mm thick. The chart, fig. 11.3 shows the passbands for a selection of materials using this criterion.

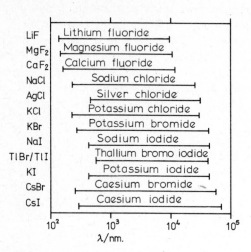

Fig. 11.3. Limiting transmittance of a range of optical crystals. *Rank Precision Industries.*

11.2. *Detection and measurement of very faint objects*

Late in the 1960's experimental work was started at Mount Wilson Observatory to develop a high sensitivity television system, using a 1·5 m reflecting telescope for the purpose with very satisfactory results, and development continues. Radiation measurement of incredibly faint sources may be achieved by bringing to bear items of advanced equipment already established, but the difficulty lies in detecting and locating such objects in the first place. The television technique is being developed to ease this short-fall, extending the range of detectable magnitude by about +2·5 (that is, by a factor of 10) fainter than may be detected by eye through the same telescope. There are alternative ways of finding these objects, one method, the 'blind offset' having been described in Chapter 7. Such methods are very costly in terms of observing time because a large telescope is occupied for many hours in exposing the necessary plate of the required star field.

The new system consists of placing at the appropriate focal plane of the telescope, an electronic image intensifier coupled by fibre-optic face-plates to the input of the television camera tube. Intensifier gain is about $\times 40$ and that of the tube target about $\times 100$, producing an overall gain of $\times 4000$. The whole system is packaged in four modular units, one of which comprises the intensifier and camera which is telescope mounted. Unit 2 is an electronic cubicle containing the pre-amplifier connected to unit 1, by 3 m maximum cable length to minimize noise pick-up. Unit 3 contains further electronics and may be separated from unit 2, by 9 m maximum cable length. These three units form a non-integrating television system and the fourth unit, which contains all the remote control gear and storage tubes, may be installed up to 120 m distant. Final output is to a series of television monitors wherever they are required. Two modes of output are used, one of which scans at a frame frequency of 30 frames per second (the standard U.S.A. television frame frequency). Second-mode operation integrates the received signal for any selected time between 0·1 and 99·9 seconds when the signal is on the tube target. In practice, it seems that no further gain arises after an integration period of about 3 seconds and it is interesting to compare this with maximum gain integration time of the eye, which is about 0·2 second. Put another way, if the dark-adapted eye cannot see a particular dim star in $\frac{1}{5}$ second, it will never see it.

Two storage tubes are used because the erase time of about 1 second would otherwise result in picture flicker. The integrated picture is read from one tube while the other is being erased and prepared for the next cycle and the process alternates at integration rate frequency. The system reads out from the appropriate storage tube at the standard frame rate, producing a flicker-free picture which changes unnoticed each integration cycle.

With such a sensitive system, stringent precautions are required to avoid permanent damage to the camera tube target which, for example, would be suffered by looking at a $+10$ magnitude star, through the 200 inch telescope. To protect against this, automatic gain control limits current flow to the tube target from bright peaks, which is a very valuable safeguard when slewing the telescope through random star fields with the television switched on. In use, the fastest integration time which will produce a visible result is selected for visual functions like tracking the image onto the spectrograph slit or photometer aperture and tracking must be done rather slowly because, as described, a new image is formed perhaps every second or two. A further possibility under consideration is to establish a co-ordinate position of the star relative to the slit and then to command the telescope, via its controlling computer, to lock onto the ' boxed ' star.

Television science is gaining ground very swiftly in many aspects of astronomy but this short review must be restricted to one more purpose and that is the measurement of small quantities of energy, effectively by counting photons. Several observatories have been working on two-dimensional photon detectors for some time but only recently have developments in television, image intensifiers and solid state electronics offered practical solution.

A report by the Astro Electronics Laboratory of Hale Observatories describes a system for observing very faint star fields. The required characteristics of the receptor are that noise is determined by photon fluctuation in the image, response is linear, range (of wavelengths) is wide and large information storage capacity for each element of the picture is available. A further requirement is photographic access to the television readout, with a wide variety of exposure times plus a sequence of very short exposures in rapid succession, similar to the Lallemand electronic camera (see figure 4.18). An image intensifier with a gain of $\times 40$ is arranged to stimulate a silicon target vidicon tube with a gain of $\times 4000$ to produce a total gain of $\times 160\,000$. The square, 500 line picture of 500 elements per line is scanned at the rate of 30 frames per second which gives 130 ns dwell time per element. Each scan over the frame, upon which the image of the faint field is formed, will show some elements struck by photons, that is, each such element has emitted a single photoelectron, and so generated an electron pulse. The co-ordinates of each element are known and the pulses are counted, which allows a complete record of the energy distribution over the field to be stored in the new solid state memory devices.

Photometric accuracy of around 1 per cent is expected from the system and this equals about $10\,000$ photo-electron events per element. It is estimated that using the 200 inch telescope with a single picture element subtended by 0.5 arc second measured from the primary mirror, photon detection rate could be down to 0.16 events per frame per element and this rate would detect stars of $+27$ magnitude in about 6×10^4 frames requiring 2000 seconds scanning time.

It may have been noted that the electronic developments described, and others of similar importance, do not include a telescope-riding observer, for a television readout or a stored record may be examined in a warm and softly lit laboratory where a man will be more comfortable and alert than when he is cooped up in the darkness of a Cassegrain cage during the early hours of a cold, high altitude winter morning. For this reason among others, which include vibration in the telescope inadvertently generated by observer movement, designers and astronomers are actively considering abandoning traditional observer positions on large telescopes of the future, for it could be that access will only be required for service and maintenance.

11.3. *New observatory design concepts*

The preceding developments are already in progress and will doubtlessly be improved with the passage of time, but two forward projects, existing at present only in concept, comprise new styles of telescope

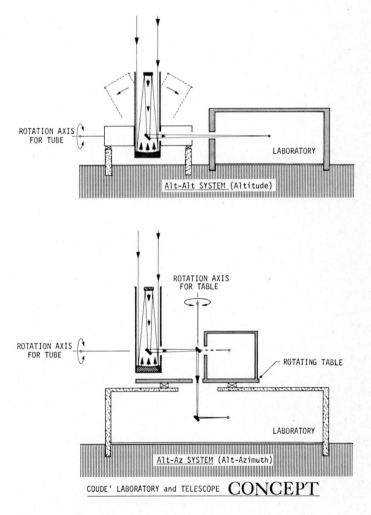

Fig. 11.4.   Two forward concepts for new forms of Observatory.
KPNO, Arizona.

197

mounting, which are fully integrated with the laboratories served by them. They are concepts originated by AURA and fig. 11.4 illustrates the principles involved.

The Alt-Alt system is shown above, where the telescope tube is rotated about two mutually perpendicular, horizontal axes to gain access to the sky within the limits set by the geometry. It is a three-mirror system of primary, secondary and diagonal flat, the latter being driven independent of the telescope, to focus at the permanent image plane within the stationary laboratory.

The alternative scheme, the Alt-Az system, is shown below and is a quasi-altazimuth system in which the telescope is rotated in elevation about a horizontal axis aligned radially upon a large turntable which supports the telescope mount on one side and a relatively small laboratory diametrically opposite. This laboratory receives the image from the telescope via a three mirror system, none of which is driven independent of the telescope. Beneath the turntable is a large, stationary laboratory which receives the images at a fixed position by introduction of a fourth mirror fixed to the turntable and a fifth mirror in fixed position in the great laboratory. In both concepts the telescope tubes are true enclosures which will permit air conditioning within; and computer control is essential to either scheme.

The Alt-Alt scheme is less costly, especially if more than one telescope is arrayed about the laboratory which is planned for several concurrent experiments catered for by one vertical and six horizontal platforms for mounting instruments almost regardless of weight or size. This is one of the great advantages, another being the minimal reflection loss of a three mirror system, especially as it is planned to use multi-layer reflection coatings on the very small secondary and diagonal flat. When the project is eventually funded and authorized, it is planned to install initially, a single telescope of 2·5 m aperture optimized for planetary work, further telescopes being added to the complex over a period of time as yet unscheduled. Note also, that there is no telescope riding observer in either scheme.

Many more forward projects are in the design offices, but enough has been described to show that new concepts and developments are endless, and so is the work load of future astronomers who will find that new fields of endeavour are opened up as the older ones are exhausted. Certainly we have come a long way since the Chaldean priests, since Lippershey's magic tube and even since Newton's first reflecting telescope.

APPENDIX I

THE highest level of expertise in optical design is ineffective unless suitable materials are available to the designer. There could, for example, have been no large achromatic doublet object lenses had it not been for the work of Pierre Guinand in producing large flint glass blanks (page 19).

Today, the glass chemist and the production technologist have combined to offer the designer a wider choice of materials than he has ever had before and a mass of data has been compiled for each of these glass types. The basic optical characteristics of refractive index, constringence, dispersion etc., are listed as one may expect, but the glassmakers' catalogues also carry a great deal of empirical information as well, which is critical to some applications. Thus one may obtain glass to a standard of purity defined by the number and size of solid and gaseous inclusions per unit volume of the glass, and to a qualitative grading of resistance to acid attack (usually 0.5 M nitric acid). Stress birefringence (two refractive index values for the same piece of glass) results from heat treatment of the material in production, but it is kept down to acceptable, defined levels published in the catalogues. The physical form of the raw material is also published, for example, moulded or pressed blanks, rolled or extruded strip.

All this, and much more is to be had from the glassmakers' catalogues and whilst each produce to the main-stream specifications, they each have their own special features.

Two sections of the Chance-Pilkington optical glass catalogues are shown. Above, a small section of an extensive range is listed together with a summary of the properties for each type of glass. Below, comprehensive details for one of the glasses listed above are shown. Many of the table columns relate directly to the preceding text, (mainly Chapters 3 and 4). The columns headed T_{25} and K_{10} relate respectively to transmittance through 25 mm of glass expressed as a percentage of incident light, and absorption coefficient for 10 mm glass thickness, each referred to the tabled wavelengths.

Glass Type	nd	Vd	nF—nC	Density g.cm⁻³	T25 λ = 400nm	Inclusion Grade	Acid Resistance	$\alpha \times 10^7$ °C⁻¹ 10°C—100°C	TA °C
623581	1.62299	58.06	0.1073	3.65	95.6	2	6.2.b	76	628
610573	1.61029	57.25	0.01066	3.56	91.3	4	5.4.a	63	638
623569	1.62280	56.90	0.01095	3.66	93.5	2	6.2.b	78	631
658509	1.65844	50.88	0.01294	3.77	84.9	3	7.1.b	82	635
TF Telescope Flint **530512**	1.53033	51.19	0.01036	2.70	95.0	3	1	67	465
BF Barium Flint **606439**	1.60560	43.92	0.01379	3.48	93.1	2	2.1.a	82	477
700412	1.70000	41.18	0.01700	4.10	75.4	2	7.1.b	75	585
ELF Extra Light Flint **548456**	1.54769	45.60	0.01201	2.95	97.1	3	1	81	478
LF Light Flint **579411**	1.57860	41.12	0.01407	3.23	96.9	2	1	80	439
581409	1.58144	40.85	0.01423	3.23	97.7	2	1	98	424

n_d	$n_F - n_C$	V_d
1·60560	0·013790	43·92

BF 606439

n_e	$n_{F'} - n_{C'}$	V_e
1·60887	0·013957	43·62

Refractive Indices

λ (nm)	λ	n_λ
365·02	i	1·64180
404·66	h	1·62989
435·84	g	1·62316
479·99	F′	1·61611
486·13	F	1·61529
546·07	e	1·60887
587·56	d	1·60560
643·85	C′	1·60215
656·28	C	1·60150
706·52	r	1·59922
852·11	s	1·59459
1014·00	t	1·59126

Transmission Properties

λ (nm)	T_{25} %	K_{10}
360	61·9	0·1919
380	82·1	0·0789
400	93·1	0·0286
420	95·6	0·0180
440	96·4	0·0147
460	97·3	0·0109
500	98·5	0·0060
550	99·0	0·0040
600	98·7	0·0052
700	98·6	0·0056
850	98·5	0·0060
1000	98·0	0·0081

Dispersion Values

Partial	λ	Relative Partial	
		F, C	F′, C′
0·007371	e, C	0·5345	0·5281
0·006726	e, C′	0·4877	0·4819
0·003274	e, d	0·2374	0·2346
0·006419	F, e	0·4655	0·4599
0·007231	F′, e	0·5244	0·5181
0·014283	g, e	1·0358	1·0234
0·006733	h, g	0·4883	0·4824

Miscellaneous Properties

Density (g. cm⁻³)	3·48
Inclusion Grade	2
Acid Resistance	2.1.a
$\alpha \times 10^{-7}$ (°C⁻¹)	82
T_A (°C)	477
T_s (°C)	667

Dispersion Constants

A_0	2·5216675
A_1	$-8·2180411 \times 10^{-3}$
A_2	$1·8950162 \times 10^{-2}$
A_3	$4·8797370 \times 10^{-4}$
A_4	$-5·0522330 \times 10^{-8}$
A_5	$1·6525807 \times 10^{-6}$

Remarks

ABERRATION OF LIGHT. An apparent displacement of the positions of the stars due to the finite speed of light and that of the Earth in its orbit. The maximum displacement (about 20·5 arc seconds) which occurs for stars in a direction perpendicular to the Earth's motion is called the constant of aberration.

ACHROMATIC DOUBLET. A two-element lens which corrects to some extent for chromatic aberration.

APERTURE RATIO. The ratio (d/f) of the diameter of a lens or mirror, to its focal length ; also called relative aperture.

ARIES, FIRST POINT OF (ϒ). The point on the celestial sphere reached by the sun, observed from the Earth, at the spring equinox.

ASTIGMATISM, OBLIQUE. An aberration of a lens (or mirror) which causes any object point off the optical axis to be focused as two straight lines at 90° to each other, and at a different distances from the lens.

BINARY STAR. A system of two stars which rotate orbitally about the common centre of mass of the system.

BLACK BODY. A body which absorbs radiation of all wavelengths incident upon it. As a radiator, at any temperature it emits energy per unit area at the maximum possible rate, and the intensity and spectral distribution of the radiation is dependent only on its temperature. Emission is in the form of a continuous spectrum.

BOLOMETER. A radiation sensing device which indicates the rate of reception of radiant energy of all wavelengths.

CELESTIAL EQUATOR. The projection of the terrestrial equator on to the celestial sphere.

CELESTIAL POLES. The projections of the terrestrial poles on to the celestial sphere.

CELESTIAL SPHERE. An imaginary Earth-centred sphere upon which the stars appear to be placed.

CHROMATIC ABERRATION. An aberration of a lens which causes light of different wavelengths to be focused at different distances from the lens.

CIRCUMPOLAR STARS. Stars in a circular area of sky which is centred on the celestial pole and has a radius equal to the smallest angular distance between the celestial pole and the observer's horizon. These stars never set to the observer.

COMA. An aberration of a lens or mirror which causes an object point off the optical axis to be focused as a comet-shaped, degraded image. In certain conditions, coma can be present in the centre of the field.

CORONAGRAPH. A special telescope which enables a photograph of the Sun's inner corona to be taken.

DECLINATION. The angular distance of an object north (positive) or south (negative) of the celestial equator, measured on a plane passing through the object and the celestial poles.

DEFERENT. An Earth-centred circle upon which the centre of another circle (the epicycle) was presumed to move with uniform motion, by which means the early astronomers sought to explain planetary motion.

DISPERSION. The separation of white light into its constituent wavelengths.

DOPPLER SHIFT. Displacement of the spectrum lines of a source due to its motion in the line of sight.

ECHELETTE GRATING. A form of finely ruled, reflecting diffraction grating in which the cross section of the ruled lines is designed to produce maximum brightness in a given wavelength called its blaze wavelength.

ECLIPSE. The passage of one body into the shadow cast by another body. Note that an 'eclipse' of the Sun would be more accurately described as an occultation.

ECLIPTIC. The projection on to the celestial sphere, of the plane of Earth's orbit about the sun.

EPICYCLE. The locus of a point in uniform motion on a circle, the centre of which is in uniform motion on the circumference of another circle called the deferent.

EQUATION OF TIME. The difference between civil time (mean solar time) and real solar time.

EQUATORIAL MOUNTING. A telescope mounting in which one mechanical axis is set parallel to the terrestrial polar axis, and the second mechanical axis is permanently at 90° to the first.

EQUINOCTIAL POINTS. The two points where the celestial equator intersects the ecliptic. The Sun passes through these points about March 21st (spring equinox) and September 22nd (autumn equinox).

FOCAL RATIO. The ratio (f/d) of focal length to the diameter of a lens or mirror ; reciprocal of aperture ratio.

HELIOMETER. A refracting telescope having an object lens split across its diameter. One half is moved, under micrometer control, parallel to the split so that two objects in the field are brought to coincidence at the image plane. The lateral displacement of the half-lens is then proportional to the angular separation of the objects.

IMAGE SLICER. A device which replaces the coudé spectrograph slit jaws. Light which normally falls upon ordinary slit jaws and is lost, is redirected by multiple reflections, to pass through the slit of the image slicer.

INTERFEROMETER, STELLAR. An optical attachment which increases the effective aperture of a given telescope. The interference fringes associated with the image of a star enable the angular diameter of the star to be deduced.

LIMB OF SUN, PLANET, OR NATURAL SATELLITE. The edge of the visible disc of the object.

LUNATION. A mean period of 29·531 days which elapses between one new moon and the next. (Note that this is not the same as the mean lunar orbital period which is 27·32 days.)

MAGNITUDE, STELLAR. The brightness of a star, planet etc., measured according to a logarithmic scale in which a difference of five magnitudes defines a brightness ratio of 100 to 1.

202

MERIDIAN, CELESTIAL. The local terrestrial meridian, projected on to the celestial sphere.

MERIDIAN, TERRESTRIAL. A line on Earth's surface, connecting the north and south terrestrial poles. Such a line is called the local meridian to a point of observation sited upon it.

NASMYTH FOCUS. The focal plane of an altazimuth or equatorially mounted telescope in which the final image is formed outside the telescope by rays reflected through one tubular elevation (or declination) trunnion, the produced axis of which is permanently coincident with the centre of the image field.

NODES. The two points on a datum plane, at which the orbit of a satellite travelling round a body located on the plane intersects the plane.

OBJECTIVE. The lens or mirror of a telescope which faces the observed object.

OCCULTATION. The hiding from view of one body by the passage of another body across the line of sight.

OPTICAL PATH LENGTH. The effective path length in terms of wavelengths ; this works out to nl where l is the actual distance, and n the refractive index of the medium.

ORBIT. The path traced by either (or any) of two (or more) bodies in motion about a common centre of mass.

PARALLAX, ANNUAL. The apparent repetitive annual movement of a near star against the distant-star background, due to the change of position of Earth in its orbit about the sun. Few stars have values > 1 arc second.

PARAXIAL RAY. A light ray which is both parallel to and very close to the axis of an optical system.

PHASE OF MOON OR PLANET. The cyclic variation of the area of the lunar or planetary disc illuminated by the sun and observed from Earth.

PRECESSION. The slow rotation of a pair of nodes or other reference points, in the same direction as the orbiting object with which they are associated.

PRIMARY MIRROR. The objective of a reflecting telescope.

PRIME FOCUS. The position of the focal plane of a telescope primary mirror.

PROPER MOTION OF A STAR. The apparent movement of a star across the line of sight, due to its motion relative to the sun in space. Most stars have very small proper motion, even measured over many centuries.

RETROGRESSION. The slow rotation of a pair of nodes or other reference points, in the opposite direction to the orbiting object with which they are associated.

RIGHT ASCENSION (R.A.) Angular distance measured eastward along the celestial equator from the First Point of Aries, measured in hours, minutes and seconds of sidereal time.

SAGITTAL PLANE. The horizontal plane which intersects the surface of a lens or mirror and with which optical axis it is coincident.

SAROS. A period of 6585 days which contain 223 lunations, (18 years, 10 or 11 days, depending upon whether 5 or 4 leap years are contained) during which a complete cycle of solar and lunar eclipses tend to recur upon the terrestrial sphere, but due to Earth's rotation, not at the same co-ordinate points.

SATELLITE. The less massive of two bodies in orbit about a common centre of mass, or all but the most massive if more than two bodies are included in the system.

SEEING.   The degrading effect on image quality which results from the transient optical properties of the atmosphere in the line of sight.

SECONDARY MIRROR.   The smaller mirror which faces the primary mirror of a reflecting telescope, and which focuses the final image at a convenient distance behind the primary mirror.

SIDEREAL.   A system of time-keeping based upon the sidereal day, which is the period of axial rotation of Earth relative to the stars.   It is about 23 hours 56 minutes of civil time.

SOLSTICE.   The time of the sun's greatest angular distance (23°27′), north or south of the celestial equator.   In the northern hemisphere, summer solstice (sun furthest north) occurs about June 21st and winter solstice (sun furthest south) occurs about December 21st.   In the southern hemisphere, the seasons are interchanged.

STANDING SIGNAL.   Constant, unwanted radiation from permanent sources which consists mainly of the sky field surrounding a faint object under observation.

TANGENTIAL PLANE.   The vertical plane which intersects the surface of a lens or mirror and with which optical axis it is coincident.

TELLURIC LINE.   An absorption line on a spectrogram, due to the presence of Earth's atmosphere between object and spectrograph.

TRANSIT.   (1) The passage of a celestial body across the celestial meridian. Circumpolar stars have upper and lower transits which occur between the celestial pole and the furthest and nearest horizons respectively.   (2) The passage of a small celestial object across the apparent disc of a larger one, e.g. Venus across the sun or Io across Jupiter.

TRANSMISSION.   A dimensionless term used to describe the passage of light through a medium or media with or without reference to the boundary surfaces.

TRANSMISSIVITY.   The ratio of flux intensity at two separated planes within the same medium which are crossed by light travelling perpendicular to them.

TRANSMITTANCE.   The ratio of incident and emergent flux intensity at the surfaces of a medium traversed by light travelling perpendicular to the surfaces.

ZENITH.   The point in the sky exactly overhead at the point of observation.

ZENITH ANGLE (OR ZENITH DISTANCE).   The angular distance from the Zenith to the observed object.

ZODIAC.   A belt of sky extending about 8° either side of the ecliptic, containing the paths of the sun, moon and planets.

REFERENCES

CHAPS. 1 and 2. V. A. Firsoff. *Facing the Universe.* Sidgwick & Jackson Ltd. 1966.
H. C. King. *The Background of Astronomy.* Watts, London. 1957.
H. C. King. *Exploration of the Universe.* Secker & Warburg. 1964.

CHAP. 3   W. H. A. Fincham. *Optics.* 7th Edition. The Hatton Press Ltd., 1965.
Jenkins and White. *Fundamentals of Optics.* Second Edition. McGraw-Hill Book Company Inc. 1950.

CHAP. 4.   Kuiper and Middlehurst. (Ed.) *Stars and Stellar Systems.* Vol. I. University of Chicago Press. 1961.
N. E. Howard. *Handbook for Telescope Making.* Faber, London. 1969
Quarterly Journal of the R.A.S. 1968. Vol. 9. pp. 98–115.
S. C. B. Gascoigne. *Journal of Physics* E: Scientific Instruments. Vol. 3. pp. 165–172. 1970.

CHAP. 5.   R. M. West. (Ed.) Proceedings of the ESO/CERN Conference on Large Telescope Design, Geneva, 1971. ESO, Hamburg 1971.
B. V. Barlow. *Contemporary Physics.* 1971. Hydrostatic bearings. Vol.12. No. 5. pp. 419–436.

CHAP. 6.   See first reference for Chapter 5.

CHAP. 7.   R. W. Ditchburn. *Light.* Blackie. 1961.
E. H. Richardson, G. A. Brealey, R. Dancy. *Publications of the Dominion Astrophysical Observatory*, Victoria B.C. Vol. XIV. No. 1. National Research Council of Canada. 1971.
Encyclopaedia Britannica Vol. 20. pp. 1172 et seq. 1972. (*Spectroscopy*)
Encyclopaedia Britannica Vol. 17. pp. 993 et seq. 1972. (*Photometry*)
Kuiper and Middlehurst (Ed.). *Stars and Stellar Systems.* Vol. II. Chicago University Press. 1961.
John W. T. Walsh. *Photometry.* Dover Publications Inc. (Constable & Co., U.K.) 1958.

CHAP. 8.   R. M. West. (Ed.) *Proceedings of the ESO/CERN Conference on Large Telescope Design*, Geneva, 1971, and 1972. ESO, Hamburg 1971, 1972.

CHAP. 9. Kuiper and Middlehurst (Ed.) *Stars and Stellar Systems.* Vol. I. pp. 1–15. Chicago University Press. 1961. (For 200 inch.)
Parsons Journal. Christmas 1965. Sir Howard Grubb Parsons Co. Ltd. (For 98 inch Isaac Newton Telescope).
M. J. Selby. *Nature Physical Science.* Vol. 240 No. 98. pp. 25–26. 1972. (For 60 inch IR Telescope.)
R. M. West (Ed.). *Proceedings of the ESO/CERN Conference on Large Telescope Design, Geneva,* 1971. ESO, Hamburg 1971. (For telescopes in progress.)

CHAP. 10. R. Wilson *et al., Nature Physical Science.* Vol. 238 No. 81. pp. 34–36. 1972. (S2/68 uv. telescope.)
ESRO/ELDO Bulletin No. 20. Feb. 1973. pp. 18–29. (TD–1A space vehicle)
Robert E. Danielson. *American Scientist.* Vol. 49 No. 3. pp. 370–398. 1961. (Stratoscope I)
Sky and Telescope. Vol. 39 No. 6. pp. 2–4. 1970. (Stratoscope II)
Daniel J. McCarthy. IEEE *Transactions on Aerospace and Electronic Systems.* Vol. AES–5 No. 2. pp. 323–329. 1969. (Stratoscope II)
NASA Technical Memorandum. NASA TM X–64726 *Large Space Telescope, Phase A Final Report.* Vol. 1. 1972. NASA, Marshall Space Flight Center, Alabama. (LST)

CHAP. 11. R. M. West. (Ed.) *Proceedings of the ESO/CERN Conference on Large Telescope Design,* Geneva, 1971. ESO, Hamburg 1971.

212

213

THE WYKEHAM SCIENCE SERIES

THE WYKEHAM TECHNOLOGY SERIES

All orders and requests for inspection copies should be sent to the appropriate agents.
A list of agents and their territories is given on the verso of the title page of this book.

†(*Paper and Cloth Editions available*)